BIRDS

KINDS OF BIRDS • HABITATS • BIOLOGY AND BEHAVIOR

BIRDS

KINDS OF BIRDS • HABITATS • BIOLOGY AND BEHAVIOR

WELDON
OWEN

Published by Weldon Owen Pty Ltd
59–61 Victoria Street, McMahons Point
Sydney, NSW 2060, Australia
Copyright © 2011 Weldon Owen Pty Ltd

Managing Director Kay Scarlett
Publisher Corinne Roberts
Creative Director Sue Burk
Images Manager Trucie Henderson
Senior Vice President, International Sales Stuart Laurence
Sales Manager, North America Ellen Towell
Administration Manager, International Sales Kristine Ravn
Production Director Todd Rechner
Production and Prepress Controller Mike Crowton
Production Controller Lisa Conway
Production Coordinator Nathan Grice

Designer Stan Lamond/Lamond Art & Design
Editor Kate McAllan
Editorial Assistant Natalie Ryan
Indexer Tricia Waters

ISBN: 978-1-74252-131-2

Printed by 1010 Printing
Manufactured in China

The paper used in the manufacture of this book is sourced
from wood grown in sustainable forests. It complies with the
Environmental Management System Standard ISO 14001:2004

A WELDON OWEN PRODUCTION

CONTENTS

A WORLD OF BIRDS

UNDERSTANDING BIRDS

BIRDS AROSE FROM early feathered reptiles by becoming warm-blooded and gaining the power of flight. Today they are the most mobile of animals. Although some never stray far from home, others cross oceans and continents. Birds have adapted to all of Earth's habitats, even the extremes of hot desert and polar ice.

Around 5,000 years ago, the ancestor of today's chicken, the jungle fowl, was domesticated.

WHAT IS A BIRD?

Birds are the only living animals with feathers. Today, there are almost 10,000 species and they display a huge diversity of colors, shapes and sizes.

Birds exist almost everywhere on Earth. They have adapted to nest in a wide range of habitats, from harsh deserts to tropical rain forests, and from Antarctica to the Arctic. Ostriches stand taller than humans, while hummingbirdsare barely larger than coins.

All birds have bills, and all lay eggs. In most cases, one or both parents incubate the eggs, although a few species bury their eggs under decaying vegetation to keep them warm. Feathers provide insulation from heat, cold and water.

Hummingbirds hover in mid-air as they suck nectar from flowers with their long, pointed bills.

Victoria crowned pigeon

Color is found not only on birds' feathers. The Victoria crowned pigeon has a colorful crest; the cock-of-the-rock has a colorful crown; and the toucan has colorful eye rings.

While many birds are fruit or nectar eaters, ospreys, like some other birds of prey, feed on fish.

Gouldian finch

Hummingbird

Hoopoe

Ostrich

Osprey

Flamingo

Cock-of-the-rock

Birds range in size from the tiny bee hummingbird to the imposing 9-foot (2.8-m) ostrich.

Emperor penguin

Toucan

King vulture

Cockerel

Toucan

13

Sinosauropteryx

Confuciusornis

THE ORIGINS OF BIRDS

The realization that birds are, in fact, "feathered dinosaurs" came about with the spectacular discovery of fossils of the oldest known bird, *Archaeopteryx*, in 1861.

Sapeornis

Birds evolved from a birdlike reptile, such as Sinosauropteryx, *to a wide range of reptile-like birds.*

The first birds appeared more than 150 million years ago, during the Jurassic period. Knowledge of their early history has grown rapidly with the recent discovery of vast beds of fossil birds and feathered dinosaurs in deposits in northeast China and central Asia. These discoveries have clarified a critical question. Birds and two-legged dinosaurs known as theropods—a group that included the fearsome carnivore *Tyrannosaurus rex*—are on the same branch of the evolutionary tree.

Toucan

Archaeopteryx

15

ANCIENT BIRDS

While the earliest bird fossils date from the Jurassic period, far more have been uncovered from the Cretaceous period (140–65 million years ago), which followed the Jurassic.

From its discovery in 1861, Archaeopteryx was considered a bird because it had feathers. Scientists still debate whether it could truly fly or simply glide.

Some of the oldest are not much younger than *Archaeopteryx* but all are much more like modern birds. Most were also undoubtedly capable of strong flight. They fell into two groups. The first had feet with one toe pointed forward and the other three backward, and a reptilian pelvis. This lineage soon died out. The second group, the ornithurine birds, had toes and hindlimbs much like modern birds—and were their immediate ancestors.

Teratornis merriami was a large, vulture-like predator that lived in North America during the Pleistocene epoch—2 million–10,000 years ago. Its fossils have been found in California's Rancho La Brea tar pits.

Several species of Hesperornis *were among the birds that lived on the late Cretaceous seas, 70 million years ago. These fish eaters may have given rise to grebes. They had lost the power of flight and, unlike all modern birds, had teeth.*

The first fossils of auks date from around 15 million years ago. More than 100,000 years ago, they were preyed upon by Neanderthal peoples. The great auk, a large flightless bird, was once widespread, but was hunted to extinction for its eggs and meat. The last breeding pair was killed on an island off Iceland in 1844.

GROWING DIVERSITY

Adaptive radiation, the emergence of different species, occurred slowly in birds. But over millions of years, a huge variety of birds has evolved.

Early in the evolutionary process, birds split into two groups. The first, and much smaller, comprised ratities, tinamous, waterfowl, guans and pheasants The second group included all other kinds of birds.

Modern birds diverged from one another about 60 million years ago. Loons, auks, gulls, ducks, cranes and petrels invaded aquatic habitats between 54 and 37 million years ago. Then, about 25 million years ago, flowering plants emerged, and insect- and fruit-eating species evolved. Between 10 and 5 million years ago, birds occupied most of their present-day habitats. As continents shifted, related birds were separated from each other and evolved differently.

The ancestors of today's loons became waterbirds between 54 and 37 million years ago.

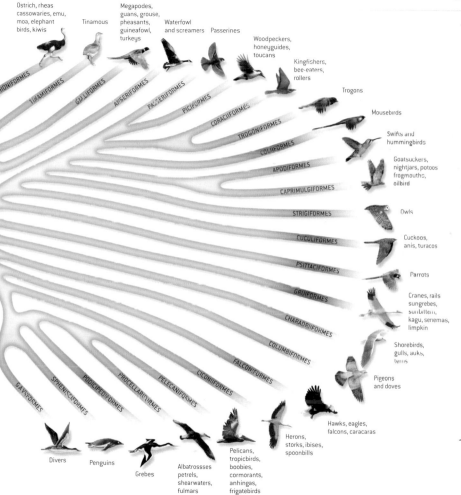

Ostrich, rheas cassowaries, emu, moa, elephant birds, kiwis

Tinamous

Megapodes, guans, grouse, pheasants, guineafowl, turkeys

Waterfowl and screamers

Passerines

Woodpeckers, honeyguides, toucans

Kingfishers, bee-eaters, rollers

Trogons

Mousebirds

Swifts and hummingbirds

Goatsuckers, nightjars, potoos frogmouths, oilbird

Owls

Cuckoos, anis, turacos

Parrots

Cranes, rails sungrebes, sunbittern, kagu, seriemas, limpkin

Shorebirds, gulls, auks, terns

Pigeons and doves

Hawks, eagles, falcons, caracaras

Herons, storks, ibises, spoonbills

Pelicans, tropicbirds, boobies, cormorants, anhingas, frigatebirds

Albatrossses petrels, shearwaters, fulmars

Grebes

Penguins

Divers

STRUTHIONIFORMES

TINAMIFORMES

GALLIFORMES

ANSERIFORMES

PASSERIFORMES

PICIFORMES

CORACIIFORMES

TROGONIFORMES

COLIIFORMES

APODIFORMES

CAPRIMULGIFORMES

STRIGIFORMES

CUCULIFORMES

PSITTACIFORMES

GRUIFORMES

CHARADRIIFORMES

COLUMBIFORMES

FALCONIFORMES

CICONIIFORMES

PELECANIFORMES

PROCELLARIIFORMES

PODICIPEDIFORMES

SPHENISCIFORMES

GAVIIFORMES

INNER WORKINGS

Every part of a flying bird's body—from its heart and lungs to its lightweight skull and hollow, light bones—is perfectly adapted to make flight possible.

Birds have fewer, and lighter, bones than reptiles or mammals. Parts of the backbone are fused together to provide a sturdy, compact frame. A bird's collarbone is also fused into a furculum, often called a wishbone. As the bird flies, this acts like a spring, bending together to store energy when the wings come down, then releasing energy on the upstroke.

Most of a bird's weight is in the center if its body where the heavy flight muscles power its wings. The ends of these muscles are connected to the wing bone and to the broad sternum or breastbone.

"Hand" extensor muscle

Ulna

Carpometacarpus

The skeleton of this macaw, like that of all flying birds, is perfectly adapted for flight. Hollow bones, a lightweight skull and a toothless bill combine to reduce weight.

Flexor flight muscles

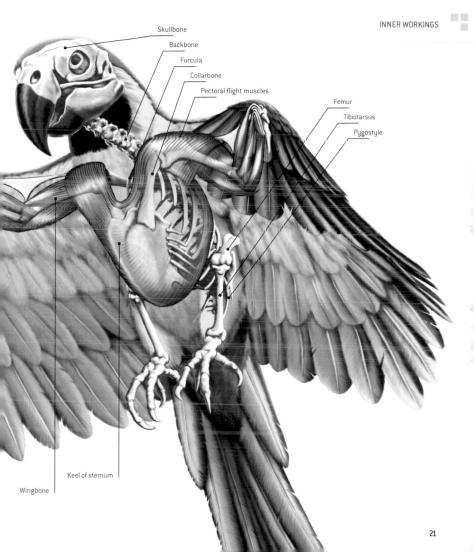

Skullbone

Backbone

Furcula

Collarbone

Pectoral flight muscles

Femur

Tibiotarsus

Pygostyle

Keel of sternum

Wingbone

FEATHERS

Feathers protect a bird from heat, cold and water, provide color for display or camouflage for protection, and are the main tool in enabling birds to fly.

Feathers consist of keratin and usually cover most of a bird's body. There are three main kinds. Closest to the body are the fluffy down feathers, which protect a bird from cold. Over the down feathers are the tougher contour feathers, which help give a bird its streamlined shape while flying.

The flight feathers on a bird's wings and tail are the most important for flying. Their vanes are locked together by tiny hooklets, so they are smooth and airtight. When the bird wants to slow down or land, it spreads these feathers to create a drag.

Eagle's down feather

Macaw's body feather

Pheasant's tail feather

Barb
Barbules
Hooklets
Shaft

Vane

Shaft

The vane of a flight feather is made up of fine strands that interlock to create a smooth surface.

Feathers provide warmth, protection, color and shape, as well as making it possible for birds to fly.

The grey crowned crane boasts a dramatic fan of stiff golden feathers. This crane, endemic to Africa, is the national bird of Uganda.

HOW BIRDS FLY

Birds are undoubtedly rulers of the skies. They fly to find food, escape from predators or migrate long distances. No other creature can fly as high, or as fast or as far.

Gliding and flapping are the two ways of flying. Soaring birds, such as vultures, hawks and eagles, exploit upward columns of warm air, known as thermals. They circle upward within the column, then glide to the base of the next thermal column and repeat the process.

Flapping flight, by contrast, adds thrust to the passive lift. Each flight feather acts as an airfoil. When the airfoils move downward, the generated upward lift propels them forward. Some birds that fly by flapping beat their wings continuously to maintain their course; others fold their wings for short periods to save energy.

Broken into stages, the wingbeat of the European robin is a smooth alternation between the wings moving upward and moving downward.

The wings are high, fully spread and thrown forward. The feathers overlap. The curled tips pull the bird forward.

The long feathers of the tail help to control the flight, especially steering and braking.

The wings are tucked well into the body during the upstroke to reduce air resistance.

At the start of the upstroke, the robin's feathers are separated. This reduces air resistance and the bird uses less energy.

The primaries convert muscle power to thrust, or forward movement.

Uplift   Uplift

Air flow

Air flow

Air flows faster across the top of the curved wing, creating a low pressure above it, and providing the lift that keeps the bird in the air.

Two sets of muscles on the breast drive the wings up and down.

The feathers twist apart at the end of the downstroke as a new upstroke begins.

The wings drop and the feathers dig into the air. This movement pulls the robin forward.

THE FASTEST BIRD

The world's fastest human sprinter boasts a top speed of about 27 miles per hour (43.5 km/h), which is slow compared with the peregrine falcon, the fastest bird.

A sailfish races into a school of fish at 68 miles per hour (110 km/h). At that speed, the impact of its long bill hitting a fish kills the prey.

A peregrine falcon's typical cruising speed is about 40 miles per hour (64 km/h), but it can get to 70 miles per hour (112 km/h). Its dive speed may exceed 200 miles per hour (322 km/h).

A sprinting cheetah reaches 45 miles per hour (72 km/h) in 2.5 seconds and may then reach 64 miles per hour (103 km/h) Very fast acceleration, not speed alone, is what enables a cheetah to overtake speedy prey.

The peregrine falcon hunts medium-sized birds, dropping down on them from above in a spectacular steep dive, called a stoop. In the mid-20th century it was almost exterminated from eastern North America by pesticide poisoning, but restoration efforts have made it a regular, although uncommon, sight in many American cities.

BILLS

Birds use their bills for obtaining and manipulating food. They are usually dull-colored, although some birds have brightly colored bills that they use in courtship displays.

Scarlet macaws use their powerful hooked bills to open nuts and fruits.

Bills vary greatly in size and shape, but in modern birds all are toothless. The size, shape and strength of a bird's bill reflect its diet. Bills are adapted, among other purposes, for tearing meat (hawks), grasping fish (terns), cracking seeds (parrots and finches), probing crevices (woodpeckers), probing in the sand (sandpipers) and straining microscopic food from the mud (flamingos). A bird's bill has four main parts: the upper mandible, or maxilla; the lower mandible; the large jaw muscles; and the horny sheath, called the rhamphotheca, that covers the bill.

Hawaiian honeycreepers have evolved different kinds of bills depending on their eating habits. The seed eaters have strong, stout bills while the nectar specialists have long, slender bills.

The massive bill of Africa's shoebill is well adapted to catching the slippery lungfish on which it feeds.

LEGS, FEET AND CLAWS

The legs, feet and claws of birds differ almost as much as their bills. Legs and feet can be long or short, and can have or lack prominent claws.

The length of a bird's leg reflects its feeding behavior and habitat. Birds that feed in shallow water have long legs, while shorebirds that feed at the edge of the waves have short legs. Seabirds have short legs that are not well adapted to walking, while ground-dwelling birds have long, strong legs.

Claws, too, provide clues to a bird's behavior and habitat. Ground-dwelling species have elongated hind claws that help prevent them sinking into mud or sand. Tree-climbing species have curved claws that enable them to cling onto rough bark. Species that tear at their prey have strong, curved claws.

Like some other non-flying birds, the emu has three forward-facing toes on its long and powerful legs.

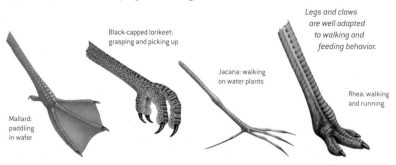

Legs and claws are well adapted to walking and feeding behavior.

Black-capped lorikeet: grasping and picking up

Jacana: walking on water plants

Rhea: walking and running

Mallard: paddling in water

Blue-footed boobies have vibrant blue feet, which they display to great effect in their courtship dances.

BIRD BEHAVIOR

ALL BIRDS HAVE fundamentally similar anatomical and physiological features. However, they display a range of nesting, reproductive and social behaviors. Most are monogamous but courting habits vary. Some prefer a solitary life; others flock together in large groups. Nests vary from a scrape in the dirt to complex structures.

Peach-faced lovebirds are monogamous and form long-term pair bonds.

SIGHT AND HEARING

Birds have the same five basic senses as humans. In most species, eyesight and hearing are the best developed and most important. Most have a poor sense of smell.

The structure of the eye is particularly complex. Unlike most other vertebrates, birds see color in an even wider range of the spectrum than humans. Nocturnal birds, such as owls and nightjars, have tubular eyes to improve light-gathering capacity without losing resolution.

Despite the lack of external ears, the hearing range of most birds seems similar to that of humans. Some species have particularly well-developed capabilities, notably the owls. The barn owl can home in on and kill a mouse in a pitch-black room within seconds because its ears are specialized for sound location.

Birds, such as this emu, have a well-developed sense of hearing, which helps them to detect predators and hear the calls of mates and offspring.

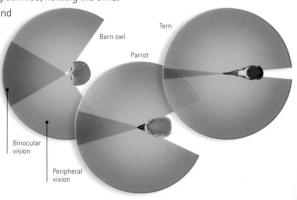

Barn owl

Tern

Parrot

Binocular vision

Peripheral vision

Barn owls, with flat faces and forward-looking eyes, have better binocular vision than other birds. Most birds, however, have good peripheral vision.

Most owls are nocturnal. Their large eyes contain more rods than cones. Rods are sensitive to low light while cones convey color information.

FINDING FOOD

This broad-billed hummingbird uses its long, thin bill to suck up nectar by capillary action.

Because of their lightweight requirements for flight, few birds accumulate large fat reserves and so they are constantly searching for their food supplies.

Whether diving for fishes, probing the water's edge for crabs, gleaning insects from the forest canopy or pecking for seeds on the ground, most birds spend a large proportion of their waking hours looking for food. Small birds, in particular, feed actively throughout most of the daylight hours.

Most birds are either solitary hunters or species that gather in groups where food is abundant, as finches, waterfowl, or penguins do—yet these birds do not assist each other. However, a mated pair may forage together and some birds that roost together may benefit by gaining information from each other about where best to feed.

Terns catch fish a few inches beneath the surface and usually dive from only a few feet above the water.

Hawks use their strong, hooked bills to tear the flesh from the live animals on which they feed.

The cedar waxwing of the Northern Hemisphere forests eats berries and fruit and will travel long distances to find its favored food.

SONGS AND CALLS

Birds sing only for each other. Some species learn their songs; some are born with them; most develop these innate, or acquired, abilities over time.

Although tiny, the yellow warbler has an elaborate voice box and a sweet, bright song.

Eurasian robins select one or more song perches, which they use for their territorial or courtship singing.

Bird vocalizations, performed by both sexes, range from simple clicks and calls to elaborate songs. The syrinx, a specialized organ that only birds possess, produces these sounds. It is located at the base of the trachea, or windpipe. All bird species give calls, which are simple sounds that serve a range of social interactions. Some birds, such as mute swans and turkey vultures, can only hiss and grunt. Parrots and mockingbirds can mimic other bird and non-avian sounds, and incorporate these into their song repertoire. Most songs function to attract mates or to interact with other species.

With its tail cocked up, its wings down and its head thrown back, this winter wren produces a remarkably loud song for a smaill bird.

DISPLAYS

Birds communicate through display activity. A display is any color pattern or physical action—or combination of these—that sends a message to another bird.

Birds use display to attract and court mates, to warn off mating rivals, to communicate with their young, to defend nests and offspring, to establish and maintain territories and to announce danger. Although plumage color and elaboration are central to much display behavior, there are often complex displays in which color plays no part. Cranes exhibit some of the most spectacular mating displays. These involve intricate and sensual dances, in which both partners jump up and down, wave their wings, dip and bow their heads, then lift their bills skyward, all the time calling loudly.

The impressive casque that projects from the top of the cassowary's head helps it push through the tropical vegetation but may also help it assert dominance.

The blue bird-of-paradise hangs upside down, spreads its wings, fluffs out its blue feathers and shows off its long tail plumes— all to attract a mate.

The elaborate tail of the peacock is at its most spectacular during the breeding season.

NESTS

Birds build nests to protect their eggs and newborns from predators and the weather, and to provide warmth for incubating eggs and their fledglings.

This red-bellied woodpecker peers out of its nesting cavity, drilled into a tree with its strong bill.

Sooty terns nest in large colonies, sometimes with up to a million nests, packed so close together that birds in adjacent nests can almost touch beaks. Species that nest on the ground, such as shorebirds and nightjars, often simply make an impression in the sand or ground. Other ground-nesters, however, build elaborate nests. Birds that nest on the water, such as grebes, gulls and ducks, build substantial floating nests that they repair throughout incubation. Hawks, owls, herons, storks and other large birds that build nests in trees construct bulky structures of sticks and branches that may last for many years.

Female sunbirds suspend their long, domed nests from a twig or leaves. The nest is decorated with spider-web, possibly for camouflage.

American robin nestlings call for food from the safety of their cup-shaped nest, woven together from grasses, leaves and twigs.

INSIDE THE EGG

During incubation a bird embryo develops into a fully formed chick and then hatches. The egg contains all that is needed for an embryo's growth.

A parent bird sits on the nest with the bare area on its belly, known as its brood patch, in contact with the eggs. This transfers the adult's body heat. An egg's hard shell must be strong enough to withstand the weight of the incubating adult.

Inside the shell are albumen, or egg white, yolk and an embryo. The yolk, an energy-rich food supply, is made up of about 28 percent fats and 20 percent proteins; the rest is water. The yolk, housed within a sac, initially acts as a stomach and intestines. Ultimately, the yolk is absorbed into the chick's body.

From the time a chick makes the first small hole in the shell of its egg, it may take between five and more than 24 hours to hatch.

Egg tooth

As they prepare to hatch, embryos develop a short, pointed "egg tooth" at the top of the upper beak. It usually falls off within a few days of hatching.

An egg contains all that is needed for an embryo's growth. The embryo breathes in oxygen and releases carbon dioxide through the porous eggshell.

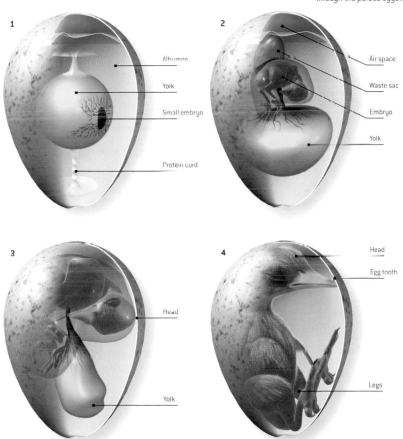

1

Albumen

Yolk

Small embryo

Protein cord

2

Air space

Waste sac

Embryo

Yolk

3

Head

Yolk

4

Head

Egg tooth

Legs

45

COOPERATIVE BREEDING

About 3 percent of all bird species breed cooperatively, meaning that additional birds—either juveniles or adults—help the parents raise their young.

There are two forms of cooperative breeding. One involves non-breeding birds only helping parents protect and rear their nestlings. The other, called communal breeding, involves some shared parenting of the offspring that are being raised together by a group of adults.

Kookaburras live in loose groups. The young from the previous year often help their parents raise the next brood of chicks.

Emperor penguins raise their chicks in a creche for protection from the cold. At six months, the chicks grow their adult plumage and go to sea.

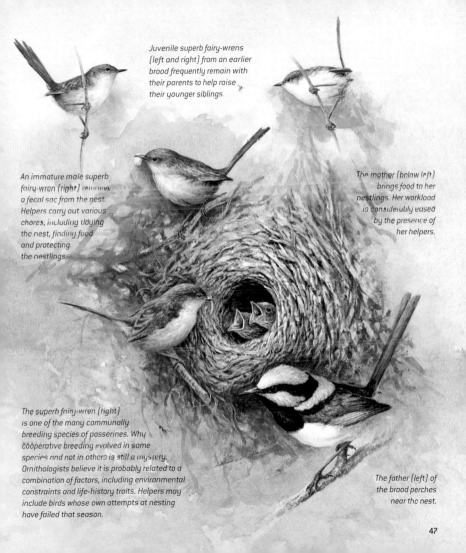

Juvenile superb fairy-wrens (left and right) from an earlier brood frequently remain with their parents to help raise their younger siblings.

An immature male superb fairy-wren (right) removes a fecal sac from the nest. Helpers carry out various chores, including tidying the nest, finding food and protecting the nestlings.

The mother (below left) brings food to her nestlings. Her workload is considerably eased by the presence of her helpers.

The superb fairy-wren (right) is one of the many communally breeding species of passerines. Why cooperative breeding evolved in some species and not in others is still a mystery. Ornithologists believe it is probably related to a combination of factors, including environmental constraints and life-history traits. Helpers may include birds whose own attempts at nesting have failed that season.

The father (left) of the brood perches near the nest.

ON THE WING

Ten major global flyways

- Arctic tern
- Short-tailed shearwater
- Wandering albatross
- Eurasian teal
- White stork
- Rufous hummingbird
- Bobolink
- Far eastern curlew & Latham's snipe
- Common cuckoo and Barn swallow
- Atlantic flyway

The migration of billions of birds every year is one of nature's great phenomena. Nearly half of the world's birds migrate, some alone, others in large flocks.

ARCTIC OCEAN

NORTH AMERICA

EUROPE

ATLANTIC OCEAN

AFRICA

PACIFIC OCEAN

SOUTH AMERICA

ANTARCTICA

The Atlantic flyway
Some 200 species of birds breed in North America in the summer months, when food is abundant, and migrate to South America in winter. The Atlantic flyway is a major migratory route, and is used by the least bittern, American kestrel, laughing gull, Cape May warbler, rusty blackbird and American redstart, among others. There are no mountains blocking this route and it provides a good source of food and water.

48

Albatrosses are at home in the skies and come to land only to breed.

S I A

PACIFIC
OCEAN

INDIAN
OCEAN

O C E A N I A

UTHERN OCEAN

Migratory birds navigate using physical and celestial features, as well as acoustic, olfactory and magnetic cues. Terrestrial birds that cross oceans and cannot land on water must complete the journey in one epic flight. To prepare, they build up their fat reserves before they begin.

There are ten major global flyways— aerial highways that link wintering areas to breeding areas. They often follow coastlines or north–south river valleys and include stopover sites, where birds can rest and refuel before moving on. Tens of thousands of migratory birds may converge on a single area in one day.

MIGRATION PATHS

Migrating birds follow the same route every year, using known mountains, rivers, coastlines, and the sun and stars, as signposts along the way.

For young birds, their first migration can be difficult. Many follow their parents; others seem to rely on an innate sense of direction. Different species follow widely different routes. Golden plovers and Hudsonian godwits, for example, take advantage of prevailing seasonal winds. Waterfowl generally migrate above prominent waterways.

Many species take indirect routes between their breeding and wintering grounds. Hawks and some other birds fly around lakes and bays to avoid long flights over water. The young of some species, such as shorebirds and hawks, migrate along coastlines, while the adults take a more inland route.

A flock of migrating birds rests on powerlines. Flying long distances requires energy and stamina.

Latham's snipe

Far Eastern curlew

Rufous hummingbird

Bobolink

Latham's snipe migrate only short distances; Far Eastern curlews travel between continents.

Rufous hummingbirds move from Alaska to Mexico; bobolinks migrate through Central to South America.

These Canada geese fly in a V-shaped formation to save energy. The rising air currents created by the leading birds provide lift for those that follow.

BIRD HABITATS

BIRDS HAVE ADAPTED to habitats as varied
as the frozen wastes of Antarctica, the hot
Sahara desert, the verdant Amazon rain
forest and the open ocean. While some live
only within one habitat, others regularly
move between more than one. Many
migratory birds occupy different habitats
in breeding and non-breeding seasons.

*Adelie penguins are one of
17 species of penguin that
make their home in the
southern oceans.*

ENDEMIC SPECIES

Some species of birds are restricted to small geographical areas, such as isolated islands or remote mountain ranges. They can survive only in a specific habitat.

These are said to be "endemic" species. Because of their isolation, or the often precarious nature of their habitat, endemic species can be vulnerable to extinction. Some parts of the world have a disproportionately high number of endemic birds. Emus, for example, occur only in Australia. Islands are particularly significant: the island of Madagascar has no fewer than five endemic bird families.

The Californian condor is restricted to a tiny range in California. It is now critically endangered; its numbers are being closely monitored through a captive breeding program.

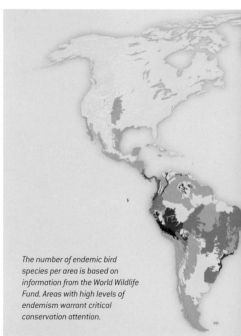

The number of endemic bird species per area is based on information from the World Wildlife Fund. Areas with high levels of endemism warrant critical conservation attention.

Native to Madagascar, the red fody is common there. It has been introduced to other islands in the Indian Ocean, such as Mauritius.

Kiwis are small, flightless birds that are endemic to New Zealand. Their short legs are placed far apart, so they waddle when they run.

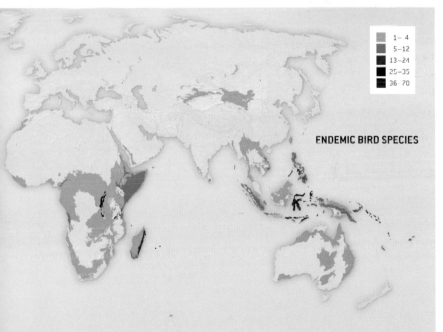

	1– 4
	5–12
	13–24
	25–35
	36–70

ENDEMIC BIRD SPECIES

OCEANS AND SEAS

Seabirds feed exclusively in the world's oceans. They obtain their food by plunge-diving, swimming or soaring on wind deflected up from the waves.

There are two main types of seabirds. Pelagic species roam the open ocean, feeding on small fish, crustaceans and squid. Coastal species forage in the mud, rocks or shallow waters around mainland or oceanic islands, where they feed on fish, crustaceans, mollusks and other small invertebrates.

Petrels, albatrosses, shearwaters and fulmars are pelagic; penguins, boobies, gannets, cormorants, puffins, gulls, terns and skimmers are coastal species. Tiny floating organisms called plankton nourish many small marine animals that in turn are eaten by the fish on which seabirds depend.

The shores of the Mediterranean Sea are lined with small shrubs, heathers and grasses, which provide well-hidden nesting sites. Little terns lay their eggs on the pebbles, where they are well camouflaged. The cliffs also provide excellent nesting sites.

Northern gannets

Little terns

Wandering albatrosses are not at home on land—their huge, slender wings enable them to wander the oceans by gliding effortlessly on wind currents.

Cory's shearwaters

Black-bellied plovers

Pied avocets

Eurasian curlew

Yellow-legged gulls

When not feeding offshore, terns loaf in large flocks on beaches. Sanderlings and oystercatchers habitually forage along the shore, and gulls patrol tidelines for carrion.

Cliffs make prime nesting sites for colonies of puffins, cormorants, murres and some gulls.

The surf zone hosts feeding cormorants and terns and, in the Northern Hemisphere, scoters, grebes, murres, loons and brown pelicans.

SEASHORES AND ESTUARIES

The seashores, bays and estuaries that border every
continent and all oceanic islands serve as a nursery
for fish and shellfish, and a foraging ground for birds.

Pelagic birds, such as shearwaters and other tubenosed petrels, usually feed on open seas.

Seashores and estuaries are varied habitats and include
rocky bays, sandy beaches, steep cliffs, extensive
grasslands, saltmarshes and mangrove swamps that fringe
the land. These are among the most productive biomes in
the world—they receive nutrients from rivers and streams,
and the tides wash away contaminants and wastes.

Cormorants, frigatebirds, boobies, gannets, gulls, terns,
herons, egrets, puffins and auks are just some of the
birds that breed on coastal habitats. Massive colonies
of thousands, or even millions, of seabirds nest in mixed-
species colonies on cliffs. Atlantic puffins catch fish near the
ocean surface and carry them back to the nest in their bills.

*The lesser yellowlegs is
a tall and graceful bird.
With its long, sharp bill
and long legs, it is well
suited to wading in
shallow water.*

Several species of duck that dive for food, such as pochards and tufted ducks, may form rafts in deep water away from shore. Divers and grebes also forage in deep water.

Shallows are sites where spoonbills, avocets and other birds gather food while wading in shallow water.

Many birds feed on mudflats. Some waders, such as common sandpipers, prefer freshwater shores.

Passing flocks of birds, such as black terns and geese, fly in distinctive V-formations.

Water rails and bitterns hide in reedbeds and forage along their edges. The reeds also provide nesting and roosting sites for a wide range of other species.

WETLANDS

Wetlands are fresh and sometimes brackish marshlands where bodies of water are interspersed with reeds and low, swampy vegetation.

To birds they are a haven, providing a wealth of fish, plants and invertebrates, as well as cover for resting and nesting. Ducks and geese have developed webbed feet for swimming and flat bills for sieving food from water. Herons and cranes have long legs for wading and long, tapered bills for striking at prey. Waders—curlews, stilts and snipe—also have long legs for wading but their bills are soft-tipped, specialized for detecting microorganisms in mud. Overhead float terns in another niche altogether, their slender bodies and wings specialized for hawking over open water and their short bills adapted to snatch fish in aerial dives.

Roseate spoonbills walk slowly with their half-open bills in water, swinging from side to side and closing on anything edible.

61

European robin

In an English forest, the Eurasian sparrowhawk attacks small birds. Its rounded wings allow it to twist and turn around the trees.

Winter wren

Eurasian sparrowhawk

Mistle thrush

Eurasian woodcock

Blue tit

Birds live on all levels of the forest, foraging on the ground or catching insects on the wing.

FORESTS AND WOODLANDS

Forests and woodlands grow wherever there is sufficient water and a suitable climate. Forests are dense stands of trees; woodlands are smaller and more open.

The blue jay is a common woodland bird of North America. It is now also found in urban parks and gardens.

The most expansive forests are evergreen coniferous or broad-leaved deciduous. Northern Hemisphere coniferous forests are called boreal forests or taiga. Their dense shade results in a poorly developed understory that provides shelter for grouse. Deciduous forests occur in eastern North America, Europe, Asia and parts of New Zealand.

Forests and woodlands generally have high numbers of birds because the complex structure of a forest provides opportunities for nesting, courting and feeding. Some species, such as thrushes, forage on the forest floor; some, such as wrens, search for insects in the understory; while others dwell in the upper branches, each exploiting the resources of its own niche.

The northern cardinal may be small—up to 9 inches (23 cm)—but its call is high and shrill. It lives in the temperate woodlands of southeastern America.

RAIN FORESTS

Tropical rain forests occur in Africa, Central and South America, Australia and Southeast Asia. More biological diversity is to be found here than in any other habitat.

The aptly named red-crested turaco is confined to the tropical forest of central western Africa.

The forests of Central and South America—including the Amazon rain forest, the largest in the world—are some of the richest. Many birds, such as the macaws, toucans and quetzals, are unique to this region. The greatest diversity of species is concentrated in the abundant light, heat and warmth of the tree canopy. Rain forests are often associated with brightly colored, showy birds, and the fruit eaters are some of the most spectacular of the canopy birds, helping to disperse seeds throughout the dense forest. Nectar feeders inhabit the lower layers, while insect eaters scuttle around on the damp forest floor.

In flight, the blue and yellow macaw is an eye-catching spectacle in the tropical rain forest of South America.

A vast array of tropical birds lives in the Central and South American rain forests. These include macaws, the resplendent quetzal and the toucan.

POLAR REGIONS

Long winter snows and freezing temperatures and winds typify polar regions. Only the upper layers of soil ever thaw. Below is permanently frozen land called permafrost.

In the Arctic, grasses, sedges, mosses and lichens grow in hummocks low to the ground; in Antarctica, only a few mosses and liverworts can survive.

Despite the rigors of sparse vegetation and extreme temperatures, some birds remain throughout the year. Ptarmigans and snowy owls are permanent residents in the Arctic. Ptarmigans stay in the same places, eking out a living on berries and snow-covered vegetation. Snowy owls travel nomadically during winter in search of lemmings; if these become scarce, they move to temperate regions to find mice. Most birds visit Antarctica only during summer, but penguins are hardy enough to stay all the year.

A skua steals an egg from a penguin's nest—a tasty treat during the breeding season.

Orcas, or killer whales, are the Antarctic's top predators. Penguins are no match for an orca on the hunt.

King penguins pursue small fish and squid. They use their flippers to "fly" through the water and can dive as deep as 1,000 feet (300 m).

GRASSLANDS AND MOORS

Grasslands—prairies in North America, pampas in South America, moors in Europe, steppes in Asia and savannas in Africa—occur where rainfall is moderate and terrain is flat.

The prairie chicken lives on the grasslands of North America. The male displays by inflating air sacs and raising feathers on his head.

Grasslands can be harsh, dry habitats with poor soils. On the African savanna, ostriches and bustards feed on plants and insects. Vultures circle above and brightly colored finches forage for grass seeds. The vast pampas of South America is home to many seed-eating species, but agriculture and industry have destroyed most of the North America and European grassland.

Grassland birds have adapted to the exposed habitat by hiding nests on the ground or in low vegetation. This protects them and their nests from predators and from exposure to the sun and winds. A few species even nest underground, in burrows.

The dry grasslands of Africa are the preferred habitat of ostriches They move around in small flocks of up to a dozen.

All animals must be resourceful to survive the harsh conditions of the African savannas. The greater honeyguide, for example, eats insects but can also digest beeswax.

Paradise whydah

Ostrich

Superb starling

Gray crowned cranes

Helmeted guinea-fowl

Greater honeyguide

A golden eagle sits on a vantage rock from where it can scan the valley.

Cliffs and screes are habitat for rock-foraging specialists, such as the common rock thrush (below), alpine accentor and elusive wallcreeper.

Alpine meadows provide productive foraging for choughs and other ground-feeding birds whenever free of snow.

Melting snow patches expose seeds and shoots on which citril finches capitalize.

HIGH MOUNTAINS

In high alpine mountains, birds survive on the edge. Not many species live there, but those that do are hardy and often specialized, and some occur nowhere else.

The kea is an unusual parrot. It is a dull and compact fruit eater that lives only in the mountains of New Zealand's South Island.

At the base of the mountain, forests may grow thickly and birds feed on seeds, fruit or insects. In warmer weather, some migrate from these forests to the alpine meadows higher up the mountain, where it is too cold for trees to grow, to forage for insects. The meadows give way to rocky outcrops and steep cliffs, and few birds live in these windswept heights. If they do, they need to defend large territories because food is scarce. Preying from the air, eagles and ravens spend much of the day in prospective soaring, especially where crags provide thermal uplift.

The bald eagle is found in a wide range of habitats, including mountainous areas. It requires large bodies of water to hunt for fish.

DESERTS

Low rainfall and humidity, strong winds, sunny days, extreme seasonal variations and abrupt drops in temperature at night are characteristic of deserts.

The roadrunner copes with cold desert nights by lowering its body temperature, so using less energy. It warms itself in the morning sun.

Some deserts are characterized by sweeping dunes and a lack of vegetation; in others, cacti or thorny bushes grow abundantly. The harshness of the conditions and the availability of food and shelter determine the species and numbers of birds. Where vegetation is sparse and water scarce, bird diversity is low and numbers are small. In deserts with a greater variety of plants, insects and reptiles can sustain a range of bird species. As well, the vegetation provides nesting and hiding places. Desert birds conserve energy by staying still and quiet during the heat of the day, emerging to feed at sunrise and sunset.

Emus' long legs allow them to cover vast distances in search of seeds, fruit and shoots. In dry times they move to new foraging areas.

In North America's western deserts, birds use cacti to help them survive. The verdin searches for insects; the gila woodpecker drills holes for nesting and hunting for insects; the elf owl nests in the woodpecker's abandoned holes; and the Gambel's quail pecks for food around the base of the cactus.

Elf owl

Cactus wren

Verdin

Roadrunner

Gila woodpecker

Gambel's quail

URBAN AREAS

Nearly half of the world's people now live in cities. Towns and cities provide a wide range of bird habitats, and many species have adapted to urban life.

Sparrows thrive in urban regions, feeding on scraps of food dropped by humans and nesting in crevices on buildings and in trees.

To live in cities, birds need food sources, nesting places and protection from humans. Most urban areas have parks, tree-lined streets, lawns and gardens. Trees, poles, houses, window ledges and rooftops are all potential nesting sites. In cities, birds can forage for insects on trees and shrubs; for berries on street and park plants; for seeds in lawns and nature strips; and for a range of foods in garbage. Many species readily accept food from humans. Starlings, sparrows and pigeons are familiar city birds. So, too, are numerous songbirds and some species of hawks, crows, jackdaws, parrots, herons and egrets.

Pigeons, or rock doves, are familiar in cities throughout the world. There are concerns that their abundance may create public health issues or drive away native species.

Almost 300 bird species have been spotted in New York's Central Park. Some are permanent residents but many are seasonal migrants

Pigeons

Northern mockingbird

American robin

Peregrine falcon

Great horned owl

BIRD-RICH HABITATS

Birds are not evenly distributed. Resources, such as food, foraging habitat and nest sites, determine how many species can coexist in one region.

Few birds can survive in the harsh polar environment. Adelie penguins are one of just two species that winter in Antarctica.

Generally the number of species, or the "avian density," is high in the tropics and low in polar regions. Species diversity decreases with altitude. For example, a mountain peak in the tropics may support fewer than 50 species; in a more temperate region lower down the same mountain there may be 200 species; while the tropical lowlands at the base of the mountain could be home to more than 500 species.

Tropical areas provide birds with abundant food supplies and have a high avian density. Rain forests are particularly rich in species.

Birds that share the same habitat often occupy different niches within that habitat. As shown in this illustration, a variety of insect eaters can forage and nest in the same European woodland because they occupy a specific niche in the habitat.

Swifts pursue insects above the treetops.

Chiffchaffs flit among branches for prey.

Spotted flycatchers dart out and seize flying insects.

Great spotted woodpeckers peck at trunks.

Common treecreepers climb tree trunks.

Wrens flit from shrub to shrub

Song thrushes search for prey in leaf litter.

ADAPTING TO HABITATS

In a famous study, English naturalist Charles Darwin used his observation of the size and shape of birds' bills as evidence of his theory of natural selection.

The vegetarian finch, one of Darwin's finches, has a short, thick beak suited to crushing buds and leaves.

Woodpecker finch

One Darwin finch species (above) has learned to extract insects from under bark or cracks in wood using a cactus spine or twig. The largest of the ground finches (below) uses its sturdy bill to eat large seeds.

Large ground finch

Warbler finch

It was Charles Darwin who first offered convincing evidence that such physical features are not immutable, and that species change over time in response to their environments. He theorized that Galápagos Islands finches, which differed most noticeably in bill size and shape, were all descended from a common ancestor and had evolved to exploit different ecological niches that were not being used by other animals. Genetic mutations that helped certain birds thrive were likely to be passed on to successive generations. This "adaptive radiation" is most noticeable on remote islands, where outside influences and competitor species are few or absent.

Modern genetic analyses have proven that Darwin was right, showing that the 14 species of Galápagos-based birds now known as Darwin's finches are indeed descended from one species, a seed-eating bunting that arrived there from the South American mainland.

Masked booby

Cactus finch

Sharp-beaked ground finch

This finch is sometimes known as the "vampire finch" due to its habit of pecking roosting or breeding seabirds in order to drink their blood.

The finch above evolved a longer bill, which allows it to feed on cactus flowers and fruits as well as seeds. Diet diversification is especially important in lean times.

79

THREATENED BIRDS

Birdlife International estimates that at least 1,200 bird species—more than 10 percent—could face extinction unless their declining numbers can be arrested.

Like many other albatross species, waved albatross numbers are in decline due to long-line tuna fishing.

Although all kinds of birds are at risk, the parrot family is facing particular pressures, with more than 80 species threatened. The habitat with the most at-risk species is tropical rain forest. Many of the threatened parrots, pigeons, pheasants, birds of prey and hornbills dwell in tropical forests. Some families, such as the antbirds of Central and South America, the broadbills of Africa and Asia, and the birds of paradise of Indonesia, New Guinea and Australia, are restricted almost entirely to forests. Species restricted to small islands are also at risk as they have nowhere else to go.

By the mid-20th century, the number of whooping cranes had fallen to crisis levels. There are now more than 200 birds.

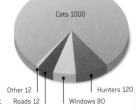

This chart shows the relative relationship between human-induced problems, shown in millions of birds killed each year.

Cats 1000
Other 12
Roads 12
Windows 80
Hunters 120

The harpy eagle was under threat 20 years ago, but populations are increasing.

The last pair of the Kaua'I O'o bird was sighted in the 1980s.

Trapping and habitat loss have endangered the golden parakeet of the Amazon Basin.

The Brazilian rain forest mitu mitu bird is now extinct in the wild. There are a few left in captivity.

EXTINCT BIRDS

Birds have existed for more than 150 million years, but it is only in the last few hundred years that massive extinctions have occurred.

The flightless moa had no wings at all. The tallest species of this group of birds grew to around 13 feet (4 m).

Over many millennia humans have hunted birds and collected eggs for food. As human populations grew, this exploitation became more acute. When people arrived on previously unpopulated islands they often hunted birds that had evolved in the absence of predators. Dodos, moas, passenger pigeons and Eskimo curlews were all hunted to extinction. The flightless great auk was one of several species that were killed to make oil for lamps. Today, introduced predators, destroyed or degraded habitats and environmental pollution—all the result of burgeoning human populations —are taking their toll on many species.

Dodos went extinct in 1681, 80 years after Dutch sailors found them on Mauritius, a then-uninhabited island in the Indian Ocean. The large birds made a tasty meal for passing sailors.

When Europeans reached North America, they found billions of passenger pigeons living in flocks miles wide. The last bird died in a zoo in 1914.

The first humans to live in New Zealand hunted moas for food, sending all ten species of these huge flightless birds to extinction within 100 years. Soon after that, Haast's giant eagles, which relied on moas for their own sustenance, followed them into extinction.

83

NAMING BIRDS

Birds' names varied from one geographic area to the next until the mid-1700s, when Carl Linnaeus devised a system for naming each and every organism.

There are 304 species of birds of prey, including Africa's martial eagle, one of the world's largest eagles.

This became the universal standard and is still in use. Each species is given a two-part Latinized name made up of its genus and species. Whereas common names vary from language to language or place to place, scientific names generally remain constant.

Closely related species are grouped in one genus; closely related genera are grouped in one family; and closely related families are grouped in one order. The resulting sequence represents the "tree" of evolution, tables diversity and provides the foundation for all biological knowledge.

Subspecies of the yellow wagtail are found in continental Europe (above) and Britain (right).

KINGDOM
Animalia
 spangled kookaburra, lion, white shark, brown snake, stick insect, human, jellyfish

PHYLUM
Chordata
 spangled kookaburra, lion, white shark, brown snake, human

CLASS
Aves
 spangled kookaburra, ostrich, vulture, chicken, egret

ORDER
Coraciiformes
 spangled kookaburra, kingfishers, rollers, bee-eaters, todies

Ibises are members of the group, or order, called Ciconiiformes, which also includes herons and storks.

The purpose of classification is to assign a unique name to each species and to place it within a structure of relationships.

FAMILY
Dacelonidae
spangled kookaburra,
white-rumped kingfisher

GENUS
Dacelo
spangled kookaburra,
rufous-bellied kookaburra

SPECIES
Dacelo tyro
spangled kookaburra

CLASSIFYING BIRDS

The arrangement of the species in the class Aves into orders and families is not only a list of relationships, but reflects hypotheses about how birds are related.

The science of classification is called taxonomy. Phylogeny is the name given to the evolutionary relationships that taxonomists hope to represent in classifying groups from a single ancestor. Ideally, all members of one bird family should be more closely related to each other than to any member of another family.

Scientists use a range of techniques in classification, including anatomical traits, plumage patterns, behavior, and analysis of egg white proteins, serum proteins, enzymes and DNA. New information, often biochemical in nature, prompts taxonomists to rethink the relationships among and within orders.

Common names can be deceptive. "True" finches belong to the family Fringillidae while this Eurasian bullfinch is in the family Thraupidae.

The plumage patterns of many species vary depending on sex. The female mallard is dull brown, while the male boasts a sleek green head.

ORDER **Tinamiformes** Tinamous

ORDER **Struthioniformes** Ostrich, emus, rheas, cassowaries, kiwis

ORDER **Galliformes** Gamebirds

ORDER **Anseriformes** Waterfowl

ORDER **Sphenisciformes** Penguins

ORDER **Gaviiformes** Divers

ORDER **Podicipediformes** Grebes

ORDER **Procellariiformes** Albatrosses and petrels

ORDER **Phoenicopteriformes** Flamingos

ORDER **Ciconiiformes** Herons and allies

ORDER **Pelecaniformes** Pelicans and allies

ORDER **Falconiformes** Birds of prey

CLASS
AVES

ORDER **Gruiformes** Cranes and allies

ORDER **Charadriiformes** Waders, gulls and allies

ORDER **Columbiformes** Pigeons and sandgrouse

ORDER **Psittaciformes** Parrots

ORDER **Cuculiformes** Cuckoos and turacos

ORDER **Strigiformes** Owls

ORDER **Caprimulgiformes** Nightjars and allies

ORDER **Apodiformes** Hummingbirds and swifts

ORDER **Coliiformes** Mousebirds

ORDER **Trogoniformes** Trogons

ORDER **Coraciiformes** Kingfishers and allies

ORDER **Piciformes** Woodpeckers and allies

ORDER **Passeriformes** Passerines

Brown kiwi

Reeve's pheasant

Rockhopper penguin

Gray-headed albatross

Brown pelican

Osprey

Eastern rosella

Barn owl

Ruby-throated hummingbird

Yellow-billed hornbill

Splendid fairywren

NON-PASSERINES

THERE IS NO SINGLE AGREED classification for birds. Different systems place birds in between 160 and 200 families in 24 to 31 orders. However, ornithologists agree that there are two broad groupings. Passerines are the largest order and make up about 60 percent of birds. All other bird orders are grouped together as non-passerines.

The green-backed heron sometimes lures fish in with an insect or twig.

RATITES AND TINAMOUS

Ratites are huge, flightless birds with flat breastbones that lack the prominent, keel-like sternums of flying birds. They occur only in the Southern Hemisphere.

These birds inhabit woodlands, grasslands, jungles and mountains in the Southern Hemisphere.

Like other flightless birds, ratites are believed to have lost the ability to fly because they either lacked predators or could evade them by their size and fast legs. The surviving ratites include ostriches, rheas, emus, cassowaries and kiwis. Most are large, long-legged diurnal birds; New Zealand's kiwis, the exception, are nocturnal forest birds with short legs. Ratites' bodies are covered in shaggy feathers. Males usually incubate the eggs and provide paternal care.

Tinamous are a related group of flying birds with keeled sternums that share some unusual anatomical characteristics—such as a distinctive palate and jaw structure—with ratites.

CLASS	*Aves*
ORDERS	3
FAMILIES	5
GENERA	15
SPECIES	60

The nostrils of the kiwi open at the tip of the bill. It has a keen sense of smell to find grubs and worms.

Ostriches avoid predators on the African savanna by outrunning them.

Australia's large, flightless emu lives a nomadic existence, continually on the move in search of the insects and vegetation on which it feeds.

The brush turkey is a rain forest bird of eastern Australia. It lays its eggs in a heat-generating mound of decaying vegetable matter.

GAMEBIRDS

These familiar birds include chickens (domesticated forms of the southeast Asian red jungle fowl), turkeys, quail, pheasants, partridges and grouse.

Gamebirds are widely distributed, although some groups are restricted to specific habitats.

Gamebirds vary in size, but all have stocky frames, small heads with stout pointed bills for pecking food and short, broad wings. They feed on the ground on vegetable matter and typically flush in low and fast whirring flight. They are the favorite prey of many predators. To elude them, gamebirds rely on camouflage from their patterned plumage, or fly or scurry away quickly. They are often polygamous and have clutches of up to 20 plain, creamy or black-spotted eggs, but species' populations fluctuate greatly. Most are grain feeders, with a crop for storing food and a muscular stomach to grind it.

CLASS	Aves
ORDER	Galliformes
FAMILIES	5
GENERA	80
SPECIES	290

Both sexes of the California quail wear the unusually shaped top knot but the female is otherwise duller.

The crested francolin is common in eastern Africa south of Sudan in dry woodland and bush.

GAMEBIRDS • Pheasants

Most species of pheasants are ground-dwelling forest birds. Their natural range is mainland Asia, although they have been introduced to many other regions.

Pheasants are medium to large birds. All males are spectacularly colored and adorned with vivid plumes for use in their elaborate courtship displays. These birds eat a diet of seeds, fruit, buds and roots, supplemented by worms, mollusks and insects. Each species has its own courtship routine, but perhaps the most impressive is that of the great argus pheasant. The male clears a hilltop in the forest, from where he gives loud cries to attract females. When a potential mate appears, he dances around her, throwing up his wings into two enormous fans of golden decorated "eyes."

The iridescent head pluage and red wattles are distinctive features of the common pheasant. Its range includes much of mainland Asia.

The female common pheasant has inconspicuous brown plumage that helps protect it from predators.

Reeve's pheasant is restricted to hill forests in central China. For many centuries its tail feathers were used as a decorative, ceremonial or religious motif.

Pheasants forage on the ground for seeds and invertebrates. When surprised, they can fly over short distances to escape.

The beautiful colors and display of the peacock's tail have but one purpose— to attract the attention of the much duller female.

GAMEBIRDS • Peafowl

Brilliance of plumage and ease of domestication have brought the peacock, or male peafowl, into the great parks and gardens of the world.

The Indian peafowl is the most common; its males have a rich, glossy blue head and neck. The pride of a peacock's plumage is his great, eye-patterned tail-train. These feathers, not true tail feathers, actually arise from the lower rump. In display they are first thrown vertically up, then shimmered out sideways in a huge fan.

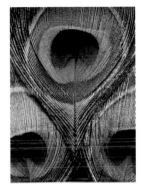

A close-up view shows the intricate color and patterning of the peacock's tail feathers.

The peacock's iridescent colors are produced by layers of clear structural keratin over dull, blackish pigment in the feather barbules. The keratin reflects colors of the rainbow not absorbed by the underlying pigment to create the patterns and tones of the plumage.

When displayed, the peacock's fanlike train is more than twice as long as the rest of its body.

99

WATERFOWL

Waterfowl live in lakes, ponds and rivers, and along coastal marshes and bays. Geese, swans, ducks and screamers make up this large group.

Waterfowl are found worldwide except for the extremes of Antarctica and the African deserts.

Ducks and geese were raised for food more than 4,500 years ago. Swans have also been kept in captivity because of their beauty and grace. Several species of waterfowl are flightless, but the rest are powerful fliers; many northern species migrate in flocks over great distances. In the air, they flap their wings continuously and can attain speeds of 70 miles per hour (125 km/h). Some have been observed at an altitude of 28,000 feet (8,500 m), near the summit of Mount Everest. Some doze on water; others come ashore to rest. Their calls range from quacks to barks, hisses, whistles and trumpeting sounds.

CLASS	Aves
ORDER	Anseriformes
FAMILIES	3
GENERA	52
SPECIES	162

The male mandarin duck, shown here, is ornately plumaged; the female is much duller. Oddly for ducks, they nest in tree cavities.

Snow geese are migratory. They breed in the north American tundra and huge flocks winter on the coasts of the United States.

The black-necked swan of South America is the smallest of the swans. It inhabits lakes and wetlands and nests on mounds of vegetation.

WATERFOWL • Swans

Largest of the waterfowl, the eight species of swans are indigenous to every continent except Africa and Antarctica. They mate for life and even migrate together.

Mute swans are attentive to their chicks and will protect them aggressively if threatened.

Swans are large waterfowl with long necks, flattened, broad bills and dense, waterproof feathers. Of all birds thus far examined, the tundra (whistling) swan has the greatest number of feathers—more than 25,000—most of which are on the head and neck. Swans make a variety of sounds, including trumpeting, hissing and snorting, and not even the so-called mute swan is totally mute. They are completely at home on the water, their size and webbed feet making them ungainly on land. Swans eat water plants—upending to reach shoots on the bottom—as well as grass and the stubble of crops

The black swan is unique to Australia. In the breeding season, huge numbers gather in noisy flocks on lakes and waterways.

WATERFOWL • Geese

The 15 species of true geese are highly gregarious. They are confined to the Northern Hemisphere, with most birds breeding in Arctic or subarctic latitudes.

Geese are medium-sized waterfowl with shorter bills than ducks and swans. Most, but not all, are somberly colored. Geese can be long-lived, and some birds have reached about 50 years of age. They mate for life and even migrate together once they have paired. Both parents incubate and care for their young.

Geese inhabit wetlands, grasslands and agricultural land; several northern species, such as the pink-footed goose and the snow goose, breed on Arctic tundra and fly south to winter on marshes and farming land. They fly in V-formation, with the leader breaking the air and causing a streamlining effect.

The bar-headed goose breeds as far north as Siberia and flys high over the Himalayas to spend summer in India and Pakistan .

The shelduck is a gooselike bird that breeds in Eurasia and winters in Africa and parts of Asia. Males and females have identical plumage.

Canada geese are indigenous to the Arctic and temperate North America. They migrate to their winter grounds in a classic V-shaped formation.

Breeding colonies of king penguins, such as this one on South Georgia, can number more than 100,000 pairs. Birds huddle together for warmth.

PENGUINS

Penguins are flightless seabirds confined to the Southern Hemisphere. Several species live on the ice floes of Antarctica and nest on the continent's bleak landscape.

Penguins are distributed through the southern oceans. The most northerly live in the Galápagos Islands.

The most aquatic of all birds, penguins have remained unchanged in form for at least 45 million years. Although they evolved from flying birds, none of the 17 species can fly. Highly specialized, social seabirds, they take advantage of their streamlined bodies, which minimize drag, and small, flipper-like wings to travel underwater at speeds of up to 15 miles per hour (24 km/h). They spend up to three-quarters of their life in the sea, staying underwater for 20 minutes or more at a time, and coming ashore only to breed and molt. Penguins eat fish, krill and other invertebrates, swallowing prey underwater.

CLASS	*Aves*
ORDER	*Sphenisciformes*
FAMILY	*Spheniscidae*
GENERA	6
SPECIES	17

Chinstrap penguins live in pack-ice waters around Antarctica. They breed in colonies on ice-free rocky areas.

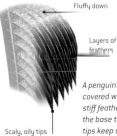

Fluffy down

Layers of feathers

Scaly, oily tips

A penguin's wings are covered with a layer of short, stiff feathers. Fluffy down at the base traps heat and oily tips keep seawater out.

LIFE ON ICE

Penguins live in some of the harshest conditions on Earth, from −80°F (−63°C) in the southern polar regions to 100°F (38°C) in the tropics, the home of the Galápagos penguin.

Penguins are superb swimmers and divers, propelling themselves with their wings, which have evolved into stiff, paddle-like flippers. They twist their flippers to provide thrust on both the upstroke and downstroke. This allows them to "fly" through the water in search of prey. The plumage is usually white on the belly to prevent prey seeing it from below, and dark on the head and back to prevent predators seeing it from above. Penguins are gregarious and forage in groups at sea. On land, they constantly shuffle about so that the shifting mass provides some shelter from the extreme weather.

Penguins, such as these Adelies, enter the water either by tobogganing down icy shores or by plunging into the frigid waters head-first.

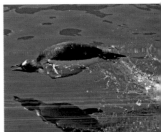

Once launched, penguins can dive deeply—they have been recorded at depths of 2,000 feet (610 m).

Penguins are ungainly on land, but underwater they are efficient swimmers and hunters.

109

PENGUINS • Macaroni Penguins

The largest of the crested penguins, macaroni penguins are named after a type of 18th-century hat. Their plume of orange feathers looked like the feathers on the hat.

The macaroni is the most common species of penguin. However, numbers have declined and they are now vulnerable.

Macaroni penguins spend most of the year at sea. In summer, breeding pairs congregate on the islands north of Antarctica in large colonies. The female lays two eggs. The first is smaller and usually only the second hatches. Both parents take turns tending this egg. It hatches after about 35 days. The male guards the chick for the first three weeks while the female collects food. Chicks then gather into crèches. Both parents feed their chick for another two weeks. By then, the young penguin's down has been replaced with waterproof feathers. It goes to sea to forage for itself.

Each year when macaroni penguins return to their nesting sites, monogamous pairs recognize each other by their distinctive calls. They perform a dance that strengthens their bond.

Macaroni penguins dive mainly for krill, but also eat small fish and squid. Chicks are fed each day.

Penguins keep some of the food they collect in their crop. They regurgitate this food for their chicks.

Macaroni penguin colonies are located on rocky slopes or beaches. A nest is at most a hollow scraped out of the mud or gravel.

Emperor penguins are streamlined swimmers—they have to be to escape from leopard seals and killer whales and dive to catch krill, fish and squid.

From below, a penguin's white front is camouflaged against the light at the surface. From above, its black back is difficult to see against the dark water below.

Stiff, slender wings act like paddles in the water, making the penguin look like it is flying underwater.

PENGUINS • Emperor Penguins

Emperor penguins, the largest species, endure the cold waters surrounding Antarctica and winter on the sea ice when temperatures can fall to −80°F (−62°C).

From March to April, emperor penguins travel across the sea ice and gather in breeding colonies of up to 25,000 pairs. In May or June, each female lays an egg and passes it to her mate, then returns to the ocean to feed. The male holds the egg on his feet under a flap of feathered skin for two months. When the chick hatches, he feeds it a milky substance created by a gland in his throat. The females return and feed the chick regurgitated fish and krill. By summer, the chicks have grown waterproof feathers and can fish themselves.

Adult penguins incubate through the winter so that chicks have the maximum benefit of a long summer feeding period before independence.

The male incubates the egg and warms the chick between his feet.

113

Great crested grebes eat large quantities of feathers. These form soft balls in their stomachs, protecting their digestive system from fish bones.

DIVERS AND GREBES

The plaintive, mournful call of divers, also known as loons, resounds over lakes in the northern parts of Eurasia and North America, where they nest.

Divers and loons are widespread. They spend most of their lives on water, coming ashore only to nest.

Although both are aquatic birds that use their webbed or lobed feet for propulsion underwater, divers and grebes are only distantly related. Physically, divers resemble sleek ducks and cormorants that ride low in the water and have pointed bills. They are thought to be descended from wing-propelled swimming ancestors and therefore may be related to penguins and petrels.

CLASS	Aves
ORDERS	2
FAMILIES	2
GENERA	7
SPECIES	27

Grebes are strong and agile swimmers, but weak flyers. Like divers, they are awkward on land and inhabit inland lakes and ponds, building their nests over the water to protect them from predators. Some are slim and elegant; smaller ones resemble ducklings.

The common loon has a streamlined body and webbed feet set far back on the body—both are superb adaptations for swimming.

Chicks ride on the back of a parent pied-billed grebe, ready to hide under its wings at any hint of danger.

COURTSHIP OF THE WESTERN GREBE

The western grebe is native to western and central North America, where it nests in colonies on inland lakes and waterways.

Grebes are monogamous. Both male and female grebes participate in nest building and egg incubation. They perform spectacular courtship dances in the water.

The courtship display of western grebes is highly ritualized. Pairs swim side by side and, as they swim faster, their bodies become more upright until they run in tandem across the water. The pair performs a "weed dance," where both birds face one another holding strands of vegetation in their bills and make a number of ritualistic displays. Then they rise and run across the water surface together. This is called "rushing." Either sex can initiate courtship and pair bonds are usually seasonal. Rival males also dance to defend their territories.

At the height of their courtship, western grebes rise in a graceful pose and, necks arched, scuttle across the water's surface together.

ALBATROSSES AND PETRELS

Albatrosses, petrels, shearwaters and fulmars, known as tubenoses, are adapted to the open ocean and spend more time over the seas than any other birds.

These are signature birds of the windswept southern oceans but one group lives in the north Pacific.

Tubenoses can glide for hours without beating their wings, and it is not uncommon for them to fly hundreds of miles in search of the squid, fish and crustaceans that comprise their diets. When albatrosses fledge from their nest, they may not return to land for six or seven years. Birds in this group can drink seawater and remove the sea salt through their salt gland.

Albatross wings are long and thin. When flying, they are kept in an outstretched position by a locking mechanism in the shoulder.

Unlike other birds in this group, the northern fulmar is a bird of the open areas of the Northern Hemisphere.

CLASS	Aves
ORDER	Procellariiformes
FAMILIES	4
GENERA	26
SPECIES	112

Albatrosses get the lift they need from winds blowing across the Southern Ocean. They can fly for hours without a single wing-beat.

MIGRATION OF THE WANDERING ALBATROSS

No other birds dominate the skies of the southern oceans like the great albatrosses, led by the wandering albatross with its enormous 11-foot (3.3-m) wingspan.

The long, slightly hooked bill is adapted for snatching squid, fish or crustaceans from on or near surface of the ocean.

Transit path of a wandering albatross

Temporary diversion to avoid particularly stormy weather close to Cape Horn

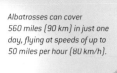

Albatrosses can cover 560 miles (900 km) in just one day, flying at speeds of up to 50 miles per hour (80 km/h).

Gliding on stiff wings, they rise and fall with majestic ease. To rise, they turn into the wind, picking up gusts which lift them up, then they pull out and soar downwind along troughs in waves, falling gradually away until they turn again to rise. This cycle continues day and night when albatrosses are on the move. When there is no wind, they sit on the sea, which is also where they sleep.

Tubular nostrils help as well. Not only do they have a strong sense of smell for finding food, but they can also monitor air pressure to pick the right wind gusts at the right moment.

Little is known of the wandering albatross' movements between breeding seasons. Some populations seem less migratory than others but the birds occur throughout the oceans of the Southern Hemisphere.

A banquet of schooling squid and crustaceans detour the albatross for some days.

These birds travel a remarkable 19,000 miles (30,000 km) in their annual migration.

June–August
Shearwaters spend their non-breeding season in the North Pacific, arriving in late June. Birds may go to the Arctic Ocean or the North American coast.

September
Adult birds take several weeks to make the return flight south to their breeding colonies in Australia, which are usually on grassy offshore islands.

October–November
After repairing their nesting burrows, courting and establishing a pair bond, the birds leave for the open sea to feed and regain condition.

Shearwaters migrate in a loop. They skirt the coastline of one continent in the spring and another in the fall.

A SHEARWATER'S YEAR

The short-tailed shearwater makes an annual journey from its breeding islands along the coasts of south and southeast Australia to the rich feeding areas of the Bering Sea near the Alaskan coast.

December–January
The egg is laid in late November and is incubated by both parents in alternate shifts, lasting about two weeks. The egg hatches in mid-January.

February–March
Both parent birds bring food to the nestling chick once every three days or so in alternating visits. The chick grows quickly and becomes independent.

April–May
The chick reaches its peak weight and puts on feathers. Parents and chick leave independently for their wintering grounds in the North Pacific.

FLAMINGOS

These elegant and graceful birds are easily recognized by their rich pink or red and white plumage, their long legs and neck, and their oddly depressed bills.

Flamingos are largely tropical and subtropical birds. They prefer salty or brackish water.

There are five living species of flamingo; the largest is the greater flamingo, almost 5 feet (1.5 m) tall. Vast flamingo flocks that congregate on the lakes of the Great Rift Valley are one of the natural spectacles of Africa. The reddish color of flamingo plumage comes from carotenoid proteins in the birds' diet of plant and animal plankton. With the lower bill acting as a trough and the upper bill as a lid, the flamingos strain the tiny organisms from shallow water or mud. Enzymes break down these proteins into pigments that are deposited in skin and feathers.

CLASS	Aves
ORDER	Phoenicopteriformes
FAMILY	Phoenicopteridae
GENERA	3
SPECIES	5

The long, slender legs of flamingos are suited to wading as they search for food.

The flamingo's hooked bill is designed for filter feeding. To feed, the flamingo bends forward, turns its head upside down and drags its open bill through the water.

The gray heron is adept at catching fish with its long, sharp bill. It waits passively until it sees its prey, then swoops silently and quickly.

HERONS AND ALLIES

This diverse group includes herons, egrets, ibises, bitterns and storks. The most unusual member of the group is the shoebill of Africa, with a head shaped like a wooden shoe.

Herons and their allies range worldwide, except near the poles and dry deserts.

Long-legged and dagger-billed, herons wade stealthily in water to stalk their prey—largely amphibians and fish—which they stab with their sharp bills. Their allies, the storks, ibises and spoonbills, probe and paddle for food, and some feed on land on reptiles and small mammals. White herons are known as egrets; their breeding plumage was much sought after by 19th-century hat-makers. Many species are gregarious, and large gatherings of several species sometimes feed, roost and even nest together. They are all monogamous and most species return to the same breeding sites year after year.

CLASS	Aves
ORDER	Ciconiiformes
FAMILIES	5
GENERA	41
SPECIES	118

If startled, a bittern will adopt this "sky-pointing" posture, trying to blend in with the reeds of its wetland home.

Great egrets were once hunted for their white plumes but their numbers are now increasing.

FISHING TECHNIQUES OF GREEN HERONS

Relative to their total body size, birds' brains are large and well developed. It is not surprising, then, that they can master complex skills.

Green herons breed in swamps and winter in coasts, where they prefer the mangroves that harbor the small fish on which they prey.

Some birds have learned unique ways of attracting prey. Green herons, relatively small birds from Central and North America, have developed a technique for catching fish. They drop leaves or small sticks into moving streams and then run downstream to snatch and eat any small fish that their "lure" has attracted. They then return upstream to deposit another small stick or leaf.

These herons carefully select sticks or leaves of a size that will swirl as they travel. This behavior is an example of tool use and indicates intelligence.

SHADOW HUNTING

Black egrets of Africa trick fish by creating a shadow with their wings. The fish are attracted to the shadow, mistaking it for a riverbank or vegetation, and swim straight into it.

Sometimes the egret makes a complete "tent" with its wings. It bends its body forward, raises its wings over its back, extends the wing tips downward and tucks its head below its wings. This tent creates an even larger area of shadow and reduces reflections on the water's surface. It improves the bird's vision at the same time as shielding it from the blazing African sun while it stands still and waits for unsuspecting fish. Thinking they have reached the safety of the riverbank, the fish gravitate to the shadow cast by the egret's wings. When close, they are an easy target.

Before the hunt, fish are wary and difficult to catch in open waters.

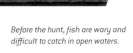

In the early morning, or when it is cloudy, black egrets do not make tents because they cannot make use of shadows. Instead, they merely walk along, searching for fish.

HERONS • Storks, Ibises and Spoonbills

The white stork, a migratory bird that often nests in pairs on chimneys in Europe, has long been associated with fertility and prosperity in folk tales.

The white stork is just one of 17 species. It is about 39 to 45 inches (100–115 cm) long, with plumage that is usually a combination of black, white and gray. The legs and bill are bright red. It wades in marshlands, snapping up food with its sharp bill. These birds start to migrate to Africa each year at the end of summer, congregating at the Bosporus in flocks of thousands in early fall.

Like storks, ibises and spoonbills are wading birds, distinguished by their long legs and long bills, which have adapted to the particular kind of food they take.

Spectacular red plumage sets the South American scarlet ibis apart from others. It forages along muddy estuaries and tidal flats.

Nesting white storks on roofs are a familiar sight in central Europe.

Spoonbills catch food in mud by sensing it with side-to-side sweeps of their paddle-shaped bills.

Male frigatebirds have inflatable scarlet throat sacs, which they blow up like balloons to attracte a mate.

PELICANS AND ALLIES

Pelicans and their allies include such diverse birds as pelicans, tropicbirds, gannets, boobies, cormorants, anhingas and frigatebirds. All are waterbirds.

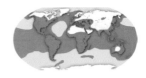

Pelicans and their allies are found in all watery environments, from open oceans to swamps and rivers.

The pouch-billed pelicans have been in existence since mid-Tertiary times, up to 30 million years ago. They all have webbed feet that allow them to move easily through water, and the webbing extends uniquely across all four toes. Many have large, naked throat sacs that are used to trap fish or as an attractant in courtship displays. Fish, as well as squid and other invertebrates, are their primary food. They breed in dense colonies on inland lakes, along coasts and on oceanic islands. Many species are monogamous and both parents incubate and care for the chicks.

CLASS	*Aves*
ORDER	*Pelecaniformes*
FAMILIES	*6*
GENERA	*8*
SPECIES	*63*

The brown pelican's bill is superbly designed to catch fish. The upper part is firm and narrow, while the lower has an enormous pouch of leathery skin into which fish are engulfed.

135

PELICANS • Cormorants and Anhingas

Within the pelican group, there are 28 species of cormorants, also known as shags, and four species of anhingas, or darters.

The double-crested cormorant is a gregarious bird of the Americas. It is noted for the bright orange skin around its bill.

These birds are superbly adapted for diving. Their feathers lack waterproofing, which allows for deeper diving; they are streamlined for fast swimming; and their legs and feet, placed far back on the body, make great propellers.

Most species of cormorants and anhingas are black and may have an iridescent green or blue sheen, while others have striking white markings. Cormorants have long bills that are distinctly hooked at the tip. Anhingas resemble cormorants, but have longer necks, longer tails and pointed, spearlike bills. One member of the family, the Galápagos cormorant, cannot fly. It hops in and out of the water to feed and nests on predator-free islands.

Cormorants and anhingas dive to spear fish. Underwater, they propel themselves mainly with their feet, assisted by their half-open wings.

Anhingas lack the oil that waterproofs birds' feathers. After diving, their plumage is waterlogged so they must stretch out their wings to dry.

PELICANS • Boobies and Gannets

It is thought that the name booby is derived from the Spanish word *bobo*, which means clown—probably because of the bird's comical courtship displays.

The red-footed booby is a bird of tropical islands, with a distinctive pink-based blue bill and red feet.

There is nothing comical, however, about the diving abilities of boobies and their cousins, the gannets. They dive like missiles, often from amazing heights, into the sea in search of their prey. Gannets even pursue fish underwater, moving with powerful feet and half-opened wings.

Most boobies and gannets have a white head, neck and underside, and are white with brown or black on the back. Colors of the soft parts of the bill and feet vary from sky-blue in the blue-footed booby to vivid red in the red-footed booby. The body is torpedo-shaped to aid plunge-diving, and the bill has a serrated edge.

Blue-footed boobies maintain their pair bonding by repeated courtship displays that involve dancing and pointing the head skyward.

Gannets nest in colonies, building nests from marine debris. They are monogamous and pair for life.

139

BIRDS OF PREY

These skilled hunters are collectively known as raptors, from the Latin word meaning "one who seizes and carries away."

Raptors comprise one of the bird world's larger orders, with members ranging from the world's fastest birds to its ugliest scavengers, and varying in standing height from 6 inches (15 cm) to more than 4 feet (1.2 m). The group includes eagles, kites, falcons, buzzards, vultures and hawks. The raptors' hunting prowess has awed humans throughout history, making them common features on military insignia and national crests. Their sharp, hooked bills are adapted for tearing flesh; their powerful feet and talons for grabbing prey; and their long-sighted eyes for spotting their quarry in daylight.

Birds of prey are found in most habitats, from tundra to tropical rain forests, deserts and cities.

CLASS	*Aves*
ORDER	*Falconiformes*
FAMILIES	*3*
GENERA	*83*
SPECIES	*304*

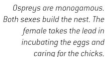

Sea eagle

Brown goshawk

Sparrowhawk

A raptor's talons match its prey. A sea eagle's long talons grab fish; a brown goshawk's grab small mammals; and a sparrowhawk's catch birds.

Ospreys are monogamous. Both sexes build the nest. The female takes the lead in incubating the eggs and caring for the chicks.

The Himalayan griffon vulture is a large bird of prey, weighing up to 22 pounds (10 kg). It feeds on mammal carcasses.

SHAPES AND SIZES

Raptors' shapes and sizes allow birdwatchers to identify them. Their wings reflect their modes of flight and ways of capturing prey.

Raptors are renowned for their keen eyesight and aerial prowess. Eagles dive on prey from great heights and can pick out a rabbit at more than a mile (1.6 km) away. Large, broad wings soar on updrafts; thin, long wings allow rapid diving in pursuit of fast-moving prey; and smaller, rounded wings permit birds to move through thick vegetation.

Diets vary from species to species and include insects, birds, mammals, fish and reptiles. Anatomical features vary accordingly. Long toes help falcons grab airborne prey. Their sturdy legs allow them to hit birds hard enough to incapacitate them. Large legs and talons help forest eagles capture monkeys, sloths and other tree-dwelling mammals in foliage.

Some raptors have broad wings suitable for soaring while looking for carrion or live prey; others have pointed wings to allow them to change direction quickly.

Andean condor
11.5 feet (3.5 m)

Bald eagle
7.5 feet (2.25 m)

Turkey vulture
6 feet (2 m)

LENGTH OF WINGSPAN

Osprey
5–6 feet (1.5–2 m)

Black vulture
4.5–5 feet
(1.25–1.5 m)

Gyrfalcon
4–4.5 feet
(1–1.25 m)

Peregrine falcon
2.25 feet (0.7 m)

American kestrel
2 feet (0.6 m)

The wing area of the Andean condor is the largest of any bird. This impressive raptor soars high on updrafts above mountain peaks and valleys.

BIRDS OF PREY • Hawks, Eagles and Kites

Members of this diverse raptor family range in size from 8 inches (20 cm) for the pearl kite to 41 inches (105 cm) for the Steller's sea-eagle.

Different species specialize in taking all sorts of prey—fish, insects, reptiles, small mammals and birds—and live in varied environments, from desert to tundra and rainforest. Despite this they have a number of features in common. They all have powerful eyesight, strong legs with sharp talons and a sharp, hooked beak. These features make eagles and hawks expert hunters, and their relatives, Old World vultures, accomplished scavengers. All these birds build stick nests, sometimes in the same locations for many years, when they create vast mounds weighing as much as a ton.

Harris's hawk is a native of Central and South America. Unlike many birds of prey, it hunts in groups and can therefore take larger prey.

The white-bellied sea eagle is a striking raptor that can snatch fish from the water with one sweep of its huge talons.

Rough-legged hawks breed each year on the North American tundra, mainly feeding on lemmings caught on the ground. They winter further south.

African harrier hawks use long flexible legs and a slender beak to probe into tree hollows and weaver nests for prey.

The great Philippine eagle soars through rain forests, catching arboreal mammals, such as lemurs, squirrels and monkeys as well as snakes and large birds. This eagle is endangered due to forest clearing.

The bearded vulture's 8-foot (2.4-m) wingspan enables it to soar on warm air currents watching for carcasses. It drops bones from a great height, breaking them and eating the marrow.

Many eagles ride rising warm air currents to save energy and travel long distances. After reaching the top of a thermal, the eagle glides down to the next thermal.

RAIN FOREST RAPTOR

Early South American explorers named these great birds after Harpyja, the predatory half-woman, half-bird monster of Greek mythology.

The harpy eagle inhabits the treetops of Central and South American lowland rain forests. It is the heaviest and most powerful of the birds of prey—its legs can be as thick as a child's wrist and, at 5 inches (13 cm), the talons are larger than grizzly bear claws.

The eagle has binocular vision and its eyes are closely set, which makes it easier to judge distance. Its owl-like face disk allows it to focus sounds. Its talons are lethal weapons. The howler monkeys recognize danger when they see the eagle but do not know which monkey will be the target until it is too late.

The whole troop sees the harpy eagle approaching and starts howling in warning.

The howls of the howler monkeys can be heard up to 2 miles (3.2 km) away.

The harpy eagle's talons are strong enough to carry prey up to half its own body weight.

The harpy eagle's talons grab the fleeing monkey.

Using its keen eyes, the eagle selects one monkey as its target.

The monkey that is the chosen prey tries to flee.

The harpy eagle flies at 50 miles per hour (80 km/h) directly at the troop of howler monkeys.

AMERICA'S NATIONAL BIRD

Because of its imposing size and character, the bald eagle is the national symbol of the United States. Fish are its main prey but it also takes waterfowl and carrion.

From a high perch overlooking a pond or stream, the bald eagle spots a fish and swoops to grab it in its strong talons. The agile eagle then carries its treasure to the water's edge or a perch, where it rips off chunks of meat with its sharp beak.

A bald eagle can focus both eyes on a single object at the same time. This enables it to judge accurately how far away prey is and adjust its attack accordingly. It also has a wide field of peripheral vision.

Strong, well-muscled legs, feet and toes make powerful weapons for snatching and crushing prey.

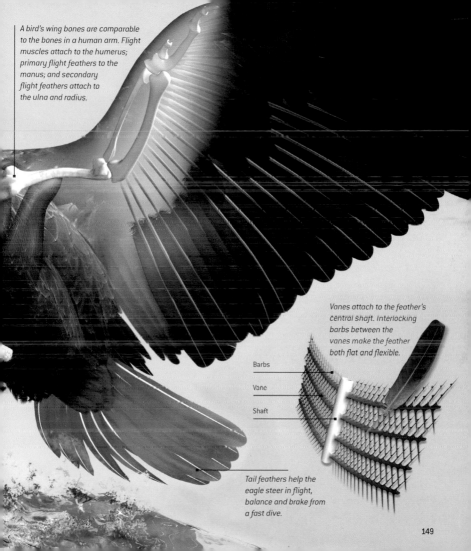

A bird's wing bones are comparable to the bones in a human arm. Flight muscles attach to the humerus; primary flight feathers to the manus; and secondary flight feathers attach to the ulna and radius.

Vanes attach to the feather's central shaft. Interlocking barbs between the vanes make the feather both flat and flexible.

Barbs

Vane

Shaft

Tail feathers help the eagle steer in flight, balance and brake from a fast dive.

149

BIRDS OF PREY • Falcons

The falcon family includes two subfamilies, the true falcons and falconets; and the caracaras and forest-falcons. Their habitats are diverse.

All the falcons share several features. They have a short neck and when they molt they shed their primary wing feathers in the same order. However, the two subfamilies have significant differences. The true falcons and falconets are swift fliers. All have a hooked, rounded upper mandible with a notch at the sides. None build their own nests: they use the nests of other birds or tree hollows, or make shallow scrapes on rock ledges. The caracaras and forest-falcons live in South America. Caracaras are slow fliers, build stick nests and do not have the notched beak of the true falcons.

Found throughout much of North and South America, the small American kestrel nests in tree cavities.

An impressive bird in flight, the striated caracara spends much of the time on the ground searching for worms, insects and fruit. It sometimes scavenges on carrion.

One of the smallest falcons, the African pygmy falcon eats mainly lizards and insects. Pairs nest in the bulky nests of the white-headed buffalo weaver.

Like other kestrels, the white-eyed kestrel of Africa hovers on fast-beating wings scanning the ground for prey. It is so fast that it can also snatch small birds in mid-air.

Falcons strike and take their prey in mid-air. Here we see the sequence of attack by a peregrine falcon: circling to scout prey (top left); the attacking dive (left); and the hit, a Eurasian oystercatcher (below). Raptors partially pluck bird and mammal prey before eating it.

ON THE HUNT

Birds of prey hunt and kill their prey in a variety of ways, although their powerful feet and sharp talons are the main weapons of all species.

The secretary bird strides across the African plains in search of prey it can subdue with a swift kick—insects and small reptiles are its staple diet.

Some pursue airborne prey; others capture reptiles and mammals on the ground. Hawks kill with their strong grips, squeezing their victims to death. Some vultures drop tortoises until they break, then swoop down to eat the flesh inside. Fish eagles and ospreys snatch fish out of the water. The unusual secretary birds subdue their prey by kicking it. And the African harrier-hawk has extraordinarily flexible legs, which it can bend at extreme angles to grope inside tree hollows for nestling birds and other small animals.

The African fish eagle spies its prey from a perch in a tree. It swoops to grab the fish in its talons and also takes turtles and waterbirds.

CRANES AND ALLIES

This ancient bird group, so diverse as to seem a bunch of misfits, comprises a range of predominantly ground-living birds that prefer walking and swimming to flying.

This group lives in wetlands, forests and deserts on every ice-free continent, and on many islands too.

Probably descended from ground-dwelling shorebirds, cranes and their relatives—rails, bustards, trumpeters, finfoots, limpkin and kagu—have filled a variety of ecological niches around the world. They typically nest on the ground or on platform nests in shallow water; eggs are varicolored. Most have loud calls, and in some species the male and female perform duets. In parts of Asia, cranes are symbols of good luck and long life; one captive crane is known to have lived to the age of eighty-three. Virtually all members of this group have been exploited for food and many are now endangered because of hunting and loss of habitat.

CLASS	Aves
ORDER	Gruiformes
FAMILIES	11
GENERA	62
SPECIES	213

The Lord Howe Island rail fell to ten pairs. It was then bred in captivity and has been released successfully.

The distinctive crest and its habit of roosting in trees set the crowned crane apart from other species.

Like other cranes, the sandhill crane flies with neck and legs outstretched. It inhabits wetlands in Siberia, North America and Cuba.

DANCE OF THE SIBERIAN CRANES

The rare Siberian crane is one of the most majestic animals on Earth. For millennia, the wetlands of northern Siberia have been home to these enormous white birds.

This species breeds in arctic Russia and western Siberia. It is a long-distance migrant, wintering in wetlands, where it feeds on the shoots and tubers of aquatic plants. Adults are white, except for a dark red mask extending from the bill to behind the eye and black primary wing feathers. The male is slightly larger than the female. It does not breed until it is five to seven years old. Unlike most cranes, it has a musical, flutelike call.

The Siberian crane is critically endangered. The world populaton is estimated to be around 3,200 birds.

With the pair standing side by side, the male (on the left) initiates the mating dance by bowing his head.

The male's head movements become more rapid; the female does not respond yet.

After bowing, the male stretches his wings and utters a lengthy cry. The female responds with a call of high-pitched double notes.

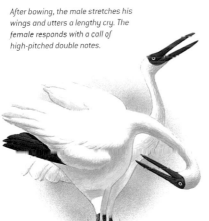

The male, head stretched back, then imitates the female's call in a lower pitch. During the dance, both birds shake their heads vertically.

CRANES • Rails

There are 133 species of rail, coot and gallinule, or moorhen, although 14 species are probably extinct. They build nests of reed stems hidden among vegetation.

The purple gallinule of North and South America has enormous feet that allow it to walk on lily pads.

Rails are small to medium-sized birds with long legs, suited to their wetland habitats. Their wings are short and rounded, reflecting their ground-living habits. Some species—notably those on islands—have lost the ability to fly. They are secretive, cautious birds. A wide variety of food is consumed, including insects, amphibians, nestling birds and small mammals.

Almost every major wetland on all continents and many islands is home to a species of rail, coot or gallinule. The absence of terrestrial predators led to many island species becoming flightless. The introduction of predators in relatively recent times has seen the extinction of a number of species.

Almost every freshwater habitat is home to the moorhen. An adult (in foreground with red bill) and juvenile are shown here.

The flightless takehe is endemic to the South Island of New Zealand. Only 225 birds remain. New breeding populations have been established on predator-free offshore islands.

159

WADERS AND SHOREBIRDS

The world's shallow waters and shorelines teem with marine and terrestrial organisms that provide food for this group of noisy and gregarious birds.

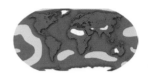

Some species live next to oceans, along estuaries or on seashores; others live far inland.

The groups within the order are diverse in bills and feet, allowing them to exploit different resources within aquatic habitats. Most live along beaches, estuaries, lakeshores and riverbanks. Typical waders, such as sandpipers and plovers, patrol shallow waters and shorelines. Gulls scavenge along shorelines, too, but with webbed feet they can swim out to feed on the surface of deeper water. Terns fly even farther out and plunge-dive for food. Auks swim underwater after prey, much like penguins. All nest on the ground or in swamps, laying mostly olive-tawny eggs mottled black for camouflage.

CLASS	Aves
ORDER	Charadriiformes
FAMILIES	16
GENERA	86
SPECIES	351

The Eurasian lapwing is common across Britain and Europe. Both male and female have crests but the male's (shown here) is larger.

The lesser golden plover, shown here in its breeding plumage, migrates from western Alaska and Siberia as far south as Australia.

Plovers are birds of coastlines and estuaries. They dash over sand or mud and feed in a "run and snatch" fashion on insects, crustaceans and worms.

Sandpipers probe rapidly for food, often in tidal flats. Their slender bills are able to sense micro-organisms in the sand and mud.

WADERS AND SHOREBIRDS •
Curlews and Sandpipers

Curlews and sandpipers inhabit seashores, especially tidal mudflats. Most are gregarious and congregate in large mixed roosting flocks at high tide.

Curlews and sandpipers share a similar structure—a long body, narrow wings and long legs—but in size they vary from the eastern curlew at about 26 inches (66 cm) to the least sandpiper at 4½ inches (12 cm).

The long downward-curving bills of curlews probe into worm burrows in mud, while the long straight ones of godwits search mud under water. Snipe and woodcock have proportionately the longest bills, and probe deep into the soft mud of inland marshes. The bills have sensory nerve endings near the tip, enabling the birds to sense food as they probe blindly. On rich mudflats, large flocks can feed together.

Extremely large eyes help the stone curlew spot crabs and other shellfish as it patrols seashores at night.

The plumage of the spotted sandpiper changes from a black-spotted breast in summer to a pale gray in winter.

The plumage of the long-billed curlew blends well with the grassy surroundings of its nest.

WADERS AND SHOREBIRDS • Gulls

Gulls a readily recognizable group, with long, strong web-footed legs for running and swimming, and long wings for their steady, sustained flight.

With a few dusky exceptions, the plumage is white with gray or black across the back and wings. Color and pattern are similar in both sexes, and young birds have mottled brown plumage with dark bills and a dark tail band.

Gulls eat a range of food, including insects, carrion and marine life exposed by tides. Larger gulls will attack and kill young or smaller seabirds. As scavengers, they have readily learnt to use waste from human activity, following boats, searching recently plowed land and feeding on rubbish tips. Gulls are sociable when feeding, and will respond quickly when the behavior of individuals indicates that food has been found.

The large and familiar herring gull is omnivorous and widespread in America and Europe.

Many species of gull take advantage of humans to gain access to food. They follow fishing boats and grab the scraps or scavenge at dumps.

Gulls are strong fliers, able to stay aloft as they search for food. They are voracious, opportunistic feeders.

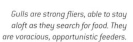

WADERS AND SHOREBIRDS • Puffins

Atlantic puffins are small seabirds that live along the coasts of northern Europe, Greenland, Iceland and northeastern North America.

Puffins are easy to recognize in summer, with their striking black and white plumage and bright orange bill. In winter, the bill loses its colorful outer sheath and dark feathers grow over the white face patches. Puffins need to eat more than 40 fish a day to survive and are adapted to life on the water. But pollution is affecting their marine habitat. Also, cats and rats have been introduced on some of their breeding islands and prey on the puffin colonies there.

Puffins can fly short distances. To stay airborne, their wings beat up to six times a second. They fly into the wind to land.

Puffins use their wings in a flying motion to swim through the water. Their large webbed feet steer.

The palate is covered with spines to grip slippery fish. This allows puffins to catch up to 12 small fish in a trip.

The bill is brightly colored only in the breeding season. Its outer shell is lost in winter, and the bill looks smaller and duller.

Puffins nest in burrows as long as 6 feet (2 m). Sometimes they use old rabbit burrows, or they may dig a burrow with their bill and feet. Inside the burrow, the female lays a single large egg. Both parents take it in turns to incubate the egg, which hatches after about 40 days. The parents fly out to sea to bring food back for the chick. Around 43 days after hatching, the chick starts to spend time outside the burrow. One week later, it fledges and is independent.

KEEPING EGGS COOL

Birds that nest in very dry habitats, such as on hot sand on remote oceanic islands, have developed strategies to prevent their eggs drying out.

A sooty tern dips down toward the waves to wet its belly.

Sooty terns dip their bellies in the ocean and carry water back to the nest to wet the eggs. As the water evaporates, it cools the surface of the eggs. The parents take turns to incubate the eggs. While the egg is incubating, a parent flies out to wet its feathers, returning quickly to the nest to prevent injury to the embryo from the hot sun. Other birds that nest near water, including gulls and other terns, also wet their nests or eggs.

Returning to the nest, it drips water from its belly onto the egg.

With little shade available, sooty tern chicks stay cool by standing in the shade cast by a young black-footed albatross.

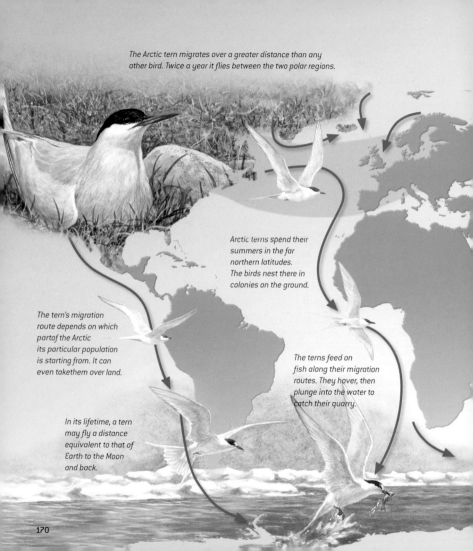

The Arctic tern migrates over a greater distance than any other bird. Twice a year it flies between the two polar regions.

Arctic terns spend their summers in the far northern latitudes. The birds nest there in colonies on the ground.

The tern's migration route depends on which part of the Arctic its particular population is starting from. It can even take them over land.

The terns feed on fish along their migration routes. They hover, then plunge into the water to catch their quarry.

In its lifetime, a tern may fly a distance equivalent to that of Earth to the Moon and back.

MIGRATION OF THE ARCTIC TERN

The Arctic tern is 15 to 17 inches (38–43 cm) long, with a short coral-red bill. The upper parts are gray. Its seasonal migrations are truly remarkable.

The tern breeds between May and August on the frigid shores of the Arctic Ocean, then migrates to the fringes of Antarctica, on the opposite side of the world, where it spends the period from November to March on the pack ice. In doing so, it passes from a northern summer to a southern one, annually accumulating some of the longest day lengths of any bird. The young terns migrate independently of their parents, and typically spend up to four years in the Southern Ocean before returning north to breed for the first time.

The Arctic tern's journey covers 12,400 miles (20,000 km) from one polar region to the other.

Environmental cues such as day length and temperature shifts tell birds when it is time to migrate. They also navigate by other cues, including landmarks, the position of the sun and stars, and Earth's magnetic field. Birds have a keen time sense that helps them judge journey lengths.

A bird innately knows it should fly at a certain angle to the sun.

In a cage where mirrors deflect the sun's angle, the bird reorients.

No matter how the sun's angle is altered, the bird flies relative to it.

Their long, powerful wings enable sandgrouse, such as this Burchell's sandgrouse, to fly quickly to water — a useful skill in dry, open habitat.

PIGEONS AND SANDGROUSE

Pigeons and sandgrouse are dissimilar in appearance. The term "pigeon" is usually used for larger species and "dove" for the smaller, more delicately built birds.

Pigeons and doves occur worldwide, except the polar regions. Sandgrouse inhabit Africa and Eurasia.

Pigeons and doves are commonplace, tree-dwelling birds that eat fruit and seeds. They have a close association with humans, who have used pigeons for carrying messages. They vary in color from the drab bluish-gray of the familiar street pigeon to the riot of hues that characterize the fruit doves of the Indo-Pacific region. Pigeons feed their young with a milky substance produced in their crops. They also have specialized bills that enable them to suck up water when they drink. By contrast, sandgrouse are dull-colored, fast-flying desert dwellers, with vestigial hind toes that help running.

CLASS	Aves
ORDERS	2
FAMILIES	3
GENERA	46
SPECIES	327

The Nicobar pigeon feeds on the ground and in the mangrove swamps of Indonesia and New Guinea.

The ornate crest of the Victoria crowned pigeon is unusual among pigeons. This species is common only in remote areas of New Guinea.

PIGEONS AND SANDGROUSE
• Doves

Small pigeons are often called doves. They feed on fruit and seeds, usually in trees, although some species feed in huge flocks on the ground.

Some species are brilliantly colored. Perhaps the most beautiful are the 47 species of fruit dove of the Indo-Pacific region. These smallish, plump birds are colored with bright greens, reds and oranges, purples and pinks, blues and golds.

The small turtle dove is common in European parks and woodland. Males "purr" to advertise their territory.

Some species have extensive ranges. The Eurasian collared dove, for example, occurs from Britain across Europe, the Middle East, India, Pakistan and China. Other species have a very restricted distribution: the whistling dove is endemic to the tiny island of Kadavu in Fiji and the Grenada dove occurs only in Grenada in the Caribbean.

The Inca dove lives in arid areas in the southwest of the US and Central America. To survive cold nights, groups of birds huddle together.

The mourning dove's name derives from it low, mournful cooing. It is a seed eater and a strong, fast flier.

The Alexandrine parakeet is confined to south and southeast Asia. Only the male has the prominent black collar around the neck.

PARROTS

Most species of parrots, parakeets, macaws, cockatoos, cockatiels, lories, lorikeets, lovebirds and budgerigars are raucous, brightly colored birds.

Parrots are birds of the Southern Hemisphere. The highest numbers live in Australia and South America.

Parrots are primarily tropical land birds, mainly from the Southern Hemisphere. Their brightly colored plumage, short necks and distinctive, powerful bills make them easy to recognize. Parrot feet have two toes pointing forward and two pointing backward, allowing them to manipulate objects well. Many parrots are gregarious, forming large flocks. Their calls are generally harsh and raucous squawks, but some species are very good mimics, particularly of human voices. This mimicry, along with their acrobatic nature and multicolored plumage, make parrots some of the most popular pets. However, trapping for the cage-bird trade has endangered many species, sometimes catastrophically.

CLASS	Aves
ORDER	Psittaciformes
FAMILIES	2
GENERA	85
SPECIES	164

Rainbow lorikeets feed on flowers, pollen and nectar. Males and females are alike in appearance.

The budgerigar is a common pet. In the wild, in Australia, they flock together in large numbers.

DAZZLING PLUMAGE

There are dull-colored parrots, but these are few. For the most part, parrots are among the most beautiful of all birds, displaying a dazzling array of bright, glossy colors.

Australia's eastern rosella has a distinctive scarlet head and throat, and bold markings and colors on the rest of its body.

Parrots' plumage colors are the result of the structural and pigmentary colors found in feathers. Structural colors are due to either interference with light (the result being iridescence) or the scattering of light, and the responsible structures are in feathers' barbs and barbules. Pigmentary colors are due to pigments. Many colors result from a combination of two or more pigmentary colors or from a combination of pigmentary and structural colors.

Green predominates in most parrots, and is effective as camouflage in the rain forest canopy where many live. Bold markings, mainly of red, yellow and blue, are prevalent on the head or wings.

A scarlet macaw cleans its plumage. This beautifully colored parrot is native to Central and northern South America.

This detail of a scarlet macaw's feathers shows the subtle color changes in individual feathers that go to make up the pattern on its wings.

BILL TYPES AND STRUCTURE

Along with colorful plumage, a parrot's bill is one of its most distinguishable features. The upper bill is always curved down, but varies in length from species to species.

The bills of parrots have greater movement and are more powerful than those of other birds. A hinge on the upper mandible provides leverage. A strong lower mandible can crack hard nuts, anchored by a crotch in the upper bill. Long bills are ideal for digging into soft wood for insects or for cutting into ripe fruit. Short, powerful bills are perfect for breaking open cones or other tough seedcases.

The unique design of their strong downcurved bill enables parrots to crush the seeds and nuts that are the diet of most species.

The blue -and-yellow macaw feeds on fruit, flowers, nuts and nectar. It uses its massive bill to open nuts and fruit.

The palm cockatoo breaks open seedcases and unripe fruit with its powerful bill and jaw.

The rainbow lorikeet uses its enlarged hairy tongue to collect nectar and pollen.

The gang-gang cockatoo holds hard-cased fruit in one foot and cracks it open with its bill.

The sharp bill of the double-eyed fig parrot is used to slice open the seeds of soft figs.

The corella's long, narrow bill extracts the seeds from cones.

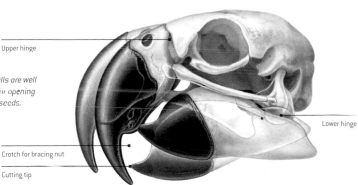

Upper hinge

Parrots' bills are well adapted for opening nuts and seeds.

Lower hinge

Crotch for bracing nut

Cutting tip

The sulfur-crested cockatoo raises its distinctive crest when alarmed or excited. It is found throughout eastern Australia and New Guinea.

PARROTS • Cockatoos

The most obvious way by which the members of the cockatoo family stand out from other parrots is that they have a crest that they can raise and lower.

In flight, this yellow-tailed black cockatoo, found only in Australia, looks almost like a hawk.

Unlike other parrots, cockatoos' coloration is limited to white, black, yellow, pink, red and orange. There are two main groups of cockatoos. The large, mainly black, ones have long, wide tails and large, powerful bills. The other cockatoos are smaller, are mainly white or pink, have shorter tails and their bills are not as large. The cockatiel, the smallest cockatoo, is in a separate genus. It does not call as loudly as other cockatoos, although it does hiss as they do when threatened. Most cockatoos eat seeds; some dig roots from the ground; and others extract grubs from wood.

Australia's galahs are gregarious birds that gather in huge flocks. They are seed and plant eaters.

183

PARROTS • Macaws

The large and brilliantly colored macaws are some of the most spectacular of the parrots. Their beauty means that many are still being trapped for the pet trade.

Despite habitat depletion and trapping, the blue-and-yellow macaw is common across its range.

The bright blue, red and green plumage of the macaws help them blend into the rain forest and woodlands where they live. They eat fruit, nuts, seeds, flowers and plant stems. Several species also eat clay scrapped from riverbanks. Scientists think that they may do this to neutralize toxins in unripe fruit. Due to trapping for the pet trade and clearing of rain forest, most macaws are vulnerable and several species are endangered, including the largest of the parrots, the hyacinth macaw, and as many as six species may have become extinct in the 20th century.

The hyacinth macaw is the largest species in the parrot family. It depends on only a few palm species for food.

South America's scarlet macaw eats seeds and fruit, even bark and sap. Its numbers have declined and in some countries it is almost extinct.

PARROTS • Monk Parakeets

Most parrots nest in cavities in trees or termite mounds. Monk parakeets take being a sociable parrot to a new level, creating vast communal nests.

The monk parakeet from the Andean foothills in South America is the only parrot that builds a stick nest. The nests are built high in trees. The birds prefer to use thorny twigs, which latch together well and may deter predators. Over a number of years more birds add nests to an original one and they grow into vast communal structures. Each pair of birds has its own entrance to a separate nest chamber. They roost in the nests all year and repair and add to them toward the breeding season. Nests weighing up to 440 pounds (200 kg) have been recorded.

Monk parakeets lay 5–12 eggs. Sometimes the previous year's young help their parents raise the next generation of chicks.

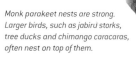

Monk parakeet nests are strong. Larger birds, such as jabiru storks, tree ducks and chimango caracaras, often nest on top of them.

Introduced to North America and Europe, monk parakeets thrive in urban conditions and often flock together in parks and gardens.

Turacos, such as this pair of red-crested turacos, often have green plumage. Their tails are long and slender.

CUCKOOS AND TURACOS

These two groups of birds are related by similarities in DNA, but the data are conflicting and the two groups differ markedly in development, anatomy and plumage.

Cuckoos thrive in a range of habitats, from moorland to rain forest. Turacos inhabit savannas and forests.

Birds of this group—cuckoos, anis, roadrunners, hoatzins and turacos— are found throughout the world except for the high Arctic, Antarctica and the north African deserts. Cuckoos are notorious as parasitical birds that trick other species into raising their chicks. However, less than half of their 140 or so species actually engage in such behaviour. Turacos, with one exception, are slender-necked birds with long tails, short, rounded wings and flattened crests.

CLASS	Aves
ORDERS	2
FAMILIES	2
GENERA	41
SPECIES	161

Roadrunners live in the southwestern deserts of the United States and often dash across roads. They eat small snakes, lizards and insects.

Cuckoos, such as this European cuckoo, eat hairy caterpillars, which most other birds avoid.

OWLS

There are two families of owls: barn owls, with distinctive heart-shaped faces and elongate bills; and "true owls," with rounded heads and hawk-like bills.

Solitary silent creatures of the night, owls are instantly recognizable by their forward-facing eyes, face masks and stout silhouettes. Owls usually roost in out-of-the-way spots. Even when out in the open, they tend to perch, camouflaged by their mottled, earth-toned plumage, so they are more often heard than seen. Their stealthy nocturnal habits, coupled with their far-reaching hoots and other eerie-sounding calls, have given rise to many folk superstitions. In lifestyle, however, they are no more than nocturnal birds of prey. They live in almost every habitat, including the frozen tundra of the Arctic (the snowy owl), at the treeline (hawk owls) and in deserts (elf owls).

Owls are widespread; some species, such as the barn owl, are among the most widely distributed of all birds.

CLASS	Aves
ORDER	Strigiformes
FAMILIES	2
GENERA	29
SPECIES	196

Apart from its fearsome talons, the owl has other specialized parts that make it a fearsome predator.

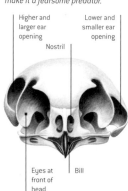

Higher and larger ear opening

Lower and smaller ear opening

Nostril

Eyes at front of head

Bill

The snowy owl, a tundra-dweller, moves to open plains in winter. It kills its prey by pouncing in flight.

The large ear tufts are a distinguishing feature of the great horned owl, a large owl that is at home in the woods and deserts of the Americas.

SUPERB PREDATORS

Most owls are nocturnal predators with soft, fluffy plumage for silent flight and excellent hearing to locate prey under cover of darkness. They feed on small mammals.

Swooping down, an owl extends its powerful legs and feet, which end in four toes tipped with sharp, curved talons on each foot. Its toes and talons close around prey such as moles and let the owl carry its meal away.

A fringe of comblike feathers on the leading edges of an owl's primary wings muffles the sound of air rushing past the swooping bird so its prey cannot hear it coming.

A special locking mechanism in an owl's feet lets the bird hold on to prey, even for hours.

When an owl attacks prey, its talons are spread out wide to increase the chance of a successful strike.

OWLS • Barn Owl

The barn owl belongs to the most specialized group of all owls. Every adaptation that owls have for nocturnal hunting seems to reach its zenith here.

Eyes are often small because the huge ears are so good at finding prey. Their lids close the eye by moving up and down, like human eyes, not forward and backward as in other birds—so owls can appear to wink. No other owl has such large ears or as well-developed facial disks for conducting sound.

One of the most widespread birds in the world, the barn owl occurs in open country and wooded areas in the Americas, Africa, Europe, Australia and Asia. Seen at night by the light of a car's headlights, the owl's white underparts, combined with its silent, hovering flight, make it appear almost ghostlike.

Barn owls are superbly adapted to gliding, swooping and grasping prey.

Rounded tip for slow, maneuverable flight

Dusky melanin bands to strengthen wings

Barn owls have a distinctive heart-shaped face and a powerful, thin, hooked bill. Their back is spotted or speckled.

The owl glides silently in for the kill.

It swoops down to its prey with talons extended to grasp and wings raised in control.

The owl catches its prey; a bite to the neck finishes the job.

Forward-facing eyes give owls the binocular vision needed to judge distances and pinpoint prey. Their range of vision is shown in yellow.

Detail of a barn owl's feather

Serrated midclaw for grooming

Burred fore-edge to silence flight

Reversible outer toes aid versatility for grasping.

Potoos inhabit woodlands in South and Central America. When roosting, they camouflage themselves by remaining still and resembling a dead branch.

NIGHTJARS AND ALLIES

Similar to owls in their nocturnal lifestyle, this group of birds—which comprises oilbirds, frogmouths, potoos and nightjars—may be distantly related to them.

Nightjars occur in a variety of warm habitats; oilbirds, frogmouths and potoos have more limited ranges.

Like owls, nightjars and their allies are active at twilight and at night. They have soft plumage in patterns and shades for camouflage in trees or on the ground. They have rather large heads and large eyes that, as in owls, are tubular and adapted to see well in poor light. But, unlike owls, the eyes are less forward-facing and the bill is wide, adapted for catching insects. To detect prey, all have a keen sense of hearing. Nightjars are named for their loud, persistent and monotonous cries that "jar" the silence of the night.

CLASS	Aves
ORDER	Caprimulgiformes
FAMILIES	5
GENERA	22
SPECIES	118

The common nighthawk inhabits varied habitats in the Americas. Like other nightjars, its mottled plumage provides effective camouflage.

Australia's tawny frogmouth is a perch-and-pounce hunter. It sits, camouflaged and motionless, until it sights its prey and then pounces quickly.

HUMMINGBIRDS AND SWIFTS

Hummingbirds and swifts are generally small, with short, weak legs. Species are widely distributed except for the high Arctic, Antarctica and north African deserts.

Hummingbirds are confined to the New World; most live in the tropics. Swifts are more widely distributed.

Any common ancestry between these dissimilar birds would have to be very old indeed. Nevertheless, hummingbirds and swifts do have significant anatomical similarities, such as the relative length of their wing bones. This is related to two distinguishing features for both groups: their very rapid wing beats; and flight behavior. Hummingbirds are also known for their tiny size, bright iridescent colors and hovering flight. The average weight of many of these birds is less than one-third of an ounce (8.3 g); the bee hummingbird is the smallest known species of bird, at a mere one-tenth of an ounce (2.5 g). Swifts are relatively bigger birds and are the fastest fliers of the avian world.

CLASS	Aves
ORDER	Apodiformes
FAMILIES	3
GENERA	124
SPECIES	429

Swifts spend most of their time in the air, using their narrow swept-back wings to help them maneuver as they hunt for insects.

The male Anna's hummingbird has a brilliant deep red head and face, and an iridescent green back. The female is much duller.

The tiny, neatly bound cup-nests of the rufous hummingbird are perched on twigs in trees and bushes.

HUMMINGBIRDS AND SWIFTS
• Hummingbirds

The most striking features of these birds are their diminutive size, bright, iridescent colors and rapidly whirring wings that allow them to hover over flowers.

The rapid wing beat (22 to 80 beats per second), coupled with a rotation of the outer portion of the wing and a powered upstroke, permit hummingbirds to hover in front of flowers during foraging. The shape of the bill reflects the type of flowers each species visits for nectar and insects. The sword-billed hummingbird, for example, has a very long bill for probing tubular flowers, while the scintillant hummingbird has a straight bill for small flowers. The tongues of hummingbirds are brush-tipped to aid in extracting nectar, but insects provide a needed source of protein and are a major component of their diet.

The male ruby-throated hummingbird gives its name to the species—it has an iridescent red patch on its throat.

The female ruby-throated hummingbird, here feeding on nectar, lacks the red throat and green crown of the male.

201

HUMMINGBIRDS AND SWIFTS
• Swifts

Swifts have a well-deserved reputation for being among the fastest flying birds. They spend most of their time in the air, feeding, drinking and even mating in mid-flight.

Swifts are mostly dark brown or sooty, with some areas of white or gray, and they have short legs with strong claws. A number of species, including the common swift of Europe and the chimney swift of eastern North America, make long and arduous migration flights to wintering grounds in the Southern Hemisphere.

All species of swift pursue and capture their food, mostly insects, on the wing. Sometimes the food ball or bolus taken to a nestling will contain up to 60 different kinds of insects and spiders, and several hundred individual prey items can be found in a single bolus.

Swifts live in the air, even sleeping there on communal "rafts" as they migrate. They also mate in mid-air as they glide downward.

Great dusky swifts flock together and fly above the crashing waters at Iguazu Falls in Brazil. They build their nests behind the falls.

The whirring sound made by the wings of hummingbirds gives them their name. The anatomy of their wings allows them to hover as they feed.

HUMMINGBIRDS IN FLIGHT

Hummingbirds flap their wings up and down to move forward.

Hummingbirds may be tiny but they are superbly adapted to hovering. Their tremendous wing muscles average up to 30 percent of their body weight.

They move their wings in a rapid figure-eight motion to hover in stationary position.

Most birds only fly forward, but hummingbirds can also fly backward, sideways and straight up or down. They can even switch direction without turning their bodies. They can accomplish this thanks to their specialized physiology and anatomy, with wings that can be turned through 180 degrees. To maintain hovering, they regularly beat their wings up to 80 times per second. Their flight feathers take up almost the entire wing, and their breastbones, to which major wing muscles are anchored, are deep and strong.

By altering the wing angle of the movements, many directional changes are possible. Here, a more up-and-down angle allows a controlled vertical rise.

The structure of the wing transfers enormous power to the flight feathers.

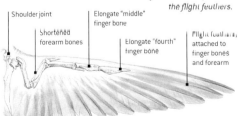

| Shoulder joint | Elongate "middle" finger bone | |
| Shortened forearm bones | Elongate "fourth" finger bone | Flight feathers attached to finger bones and forearm |

Hummingbirds flap their wings above and behind their heads to move backward.

MOUSEBIRDS

The mousebird gets its name from its odd habit of creeping and crawling among bushes and clinging upside down, with its long tail held high.

Mousebirds live in a range of African habitats south of the Sahara, from dry bushland to forest edges.

Their diets include wild or cultivated fruit and seedlings. They are therefore sometimes considered pests. They build cup-nests in bushes, lay sepia-marked eggs, and can cannibalize their young if they stray from the nest. Mousebirds dislike rain and cold, huddling together and sometimes becoming torpid to save energy.

CLASS	*Aves*
ORDER	*Coliiformes*
FAMILY	*Coliidae*
GENERA	2
SPECIES	6

Little is known of the habits of the white-headed mousebird, which is endemic to the horn of Africa.

Like other mousebirds, the red-faced mousebird is drab except for color on the face and bill, and red feet.

TROGONS

Trogons are brilliantly colored, solitary inhabitants of the tropical forests. Most have long, square tails and green plumage on their backs.

Trogons are found only in the tropics of the Americas, Africa and Asia. They live in rain forests and scrub.

CLASS	Aves
ORDER	Trogoniformes
FAMILY	Trogonidae
GENERA	6
SPECIES	39

The best known of these secretive birds is the resplendent quetzal, the national bird of Guatemala, which was considered divine by the Aztecs. Female trogons are duller than males, and lay white to buff eggs in tree cavities. Both sexes brood. Trogons are territorial, perching while they scan for food. They eat insects, snails and frogs; some species also eat fruit. Males stage displays that include chases through trees.

The streaming tail of the resplendent quetzal makes up over half its body length. The male is extravagently colored.

Trogons, such as this elegant trogon, have short bills. Their unique feet enable them to perch for long periods.

KINGFISHERS AND ALLIES

Kingfishers and their allies include the Central American motmots and todies, and the Afro-Asian bee-eaters, rollers, hoopoes and hornbills.

Kingfishers and their allies occur in a range of aquatic and woodland environments around the world.

CLASS	*Aves*
ORDER	*Coraciiformes*
FAMILIES	*11*
GENERA	*51*
SPECIES	*209*

Birds in this group vary in size, from tiny West Indian todies, at 3.5 inches (9 cm) to hornbills at 5 feet (1.5 m). Despite their diversity, all have short feet specialized for perching with three part-fused forward toes. Many species have brilliantly colored plumage, and all nest in holes that they dig in soil or in rotten trees. Kingfishers have robust, straight bills with sharply pointed or slightly hooked tips. The former is best suited for striking at and grasping fish and other prey in water, and the latter for holding and crushing prey caught on land.

The European kingfisher uses regular perches above water to preen and watch for fish to catch.

The blue-crowned motmot is a forest bird of Central and South America. It perches silently, then glides to the ground to take worms and insects.

The male rhinoceros hornbill uses its distinguishing ornate casque in fights with other males and also displays it to females when courting.

KINGFISHERS AND ALLIES
• Kingfishers

Kingfishers vary in size, from the giant kingfisher of Africa, with a length of more than 16 inches (40 cm), to the black-fronted pygmy kingfisher of Africa at 4 inches (10 cm).

The pied kingfisher is found in Africa and Asia. It hovers over water to spot prey and does not always take food back to a perch to eat.

Because the best known species, the Eurasian kingfisher, feeds mainly on fish captured by diving into a pond or stream from an overhanging branch, the common belief is that all other kingfishers do likewise. In fact, most species are generalized predators that take a range of prey from the ground or in water. A typical kingfisher bill is proportionately large, generally long and straight, with a sharply pointed or slightly hooked tip.

Their plumage is commonly bright, often with a metallic brilliance, in blues, greens, purple, reddish or brown tones, frequently offset with white patches or dark markings. The wings tend to be short and rounded.

Dagger-like bills are typical of kingfishers. Africa's aptly named giant kingfisher is as large as a chicken.

The spangled kookaburra of southern New Guinea frequents monsoon forest and woodland. It congregates in noisy groups.

KINGFISHERS AND ALLIES
• Bee-Eaters, Rollers and Hoopoes

Diet and distinctive behavior have given their names to these groups of kingfishers. Bees—and other stinging insects—are the preferred food of most bee-eaters.

The swallow-tailed bee-eater—here eating a bee—is native to woodland and grassland in southern Africa.

Bee-eaters have developed an effective technique for getting rid of their prey's poisonous venom. A captured insect is struck repeatedly against the perch, and then is rubbed rapidly on the perch while the bird closes its bill tightly to expel the venom and sting.

Rollers take their name from the twisting or "rolling" actions that characterize the courtship and territorial flights undertaken by some of the dozen species. These stocky birds have brightly colored plumage, with shades of blue predominating. They are especially prevalent in Africa, where both resident and overwintering species are conspicuousin open and lightly wooded habitats.

One of Africa's most conspicuous birds, the lilac-breasted roller has a robust bill, short legs and a squarish tail with streamers.

Hoopoes are birds of Eurasia and sub-Saharan Africa. Their large, black-tipped crest and downward-curving bill are distinctive features.

The kingfisher draws its wings back before it plunges, to streamline its body in preparation for the dive.

Kingfishers use their keen sense of sight and adjust their diving angle to account for the water's refraction.

Actual position

KINGFISHER DIVING SKILLS

Apparent position

Birds that dive into water for fish below the surface adjust their diving so that they are able to catch the prey.

If a kingfisher—or any other diving bird—entered the water exactly where the fish appeared to be, it would miss. The birds have to account for the water's index of refraction, since an object underwater is actually closer than it appears.

The common kingfisher does not only feed on fish—it will eat insects, worms and amphibians.

Not all kingfishers are divers. In fact, most are generalized predators that eat a variety of terrestrial and aquatic invertebrates and vertebrates. To hunt, they sit quietly on a perch, from which they survey their surroundings. Spotting prey, they swoop down and seize it in their bills. After bringing it back to a perch, they immobilize it by striking it repeatedly against a branch.

KINGFISHERS AND ALLIES
• Hornbills

Hornbills are large birds with massive, brightly colored bills. Communal and noisy fliers, they call in unison as their broad wings thresh the air.

Hornbills are conspicuous for their long downward-curving bills, often with a prominent casque on top, their loud calls and, at close range, their long eyelashes. They are mainly aboreal fruit eaters, able to manipulate food in the bill with great dexterity. Clockwise from top, southern ground hornbill, wreathed hornbill and calao rufous hornbill.

The rhinoceros hornbill is a monogomous and territorial bird of the Southeast Asian rain forest. It nests in large hollows in the trees. For protection, the brooding female walls herself into the nest hole with mud and droppings. During the day, the male feeds fruit and insects to the female bird through a small hole in the entrance for the period of incubation and rearing, which can be up to 100 days.

Spot-backed puffbirds live in dry forest in Brazil. They nest in burrows they dig into banks or even level ground.

JACAMARS AND PUFFBIRDS

Jacamars and puffbirds are graceful, tree-dwelling, forest birds with long, slender bills for catching insects on the wing, including butterflies.

These are forest dwellers of Central and northern South America. Most live in the Amazon rain forests.

Because these species have a foot with two toes pointing forward and two backward, they have usually been associated with woodpeckers and their allies. Yet, they have other traits that link them to the kingfishers and rollers, particularly in their head bones. Like many kingfisher allies, they dig burrows in the ground for nesting, have long incubation periods, and their nest sanitation is poor. Their eggs are plain white. Although recent DNA studies are noncommittal as to where these species belong, the jacamars and puffbirds have been placed in the same order as the woodpeckers—for the time being at least!

CLASS	Aves
ORDER	Piciformes
FAMILIES	2
GENERA	15
SPECIES	51

The long bill and tail, compact shape and iridescent colors are typical of the rufous-tailed jacamar.

Puffbirds are silent birds in dull gray or brown plumage, with stout bills. They often squat motionless on a branch, like an unobtrusive ball of feathers.

WOODPECKERS AND ALLIES

These three families of birds—barbets and toucans; honeyguides; and woodpeckers—may look different; but they share certain anatomical features.

Woodpeckers are widespread; barbets and toucans are tropical and honeyguides inhabit Africa ad Asia.

All have so-called zygodactyl feet, with two toes pointing forward and two pointing back, which allows them to grip vertical tree trunks. They also all lack down feathers and lay white eggs. Most species are colorful; some are even gaudy. They are primarily tropical birds that live in trees and nest in their cavities, in termite mounds or in the ground. Woodpeckers and barbets typically excavate their own nest holes in trees; their abandoned holes are then often used by other species. Woodpeckers sometimes live within sight of large cities and are frequent visitors to bird-feeding stations.

CLASS	*Aves*
ORDER	*Piciformes*
FAMILIES	*2*
GENERA	*53*
SPECIES	*347*

The northern flicker is the most common and conspicuous large woodpecker in much of North America.

The red and yellow barbet uses its bill to seize insects, fruit and even young birds from the scrublands of central east Africa.

The pileated woodpecker is loud and conspicuous. It eats mainly ants, which it extracts with its bill from rotting trees and fallen logs.

The toucan's bill has an internal structure rather like honeycomb to keep it light. It can reach branches too thin to support the bird's weight.

WOODPECKERS • Toucans

The comical-looking toucans of tropical America are distinctive because of their large size, frilled tongue, and colorfully patterned and often serrated bill.

South America's channel-billed toucan has a crimson breast and dark bill.

Most toucans are black, blue, green, brown, yellow or red, with brilliantly colored stripes or patches on the bill, and often bright, bare skin around the eyes. The function of the enormous bill is uncertain, but it is very light; the thin outer shell is supported internally by a spongy web of bony struts and tissue. In flight, toucans appear ungainly and conspicuous but, like parrots, they are surprisingly inconspicuous when perched in a tree, unless they are calling or displaying. They feed on fruit, moving long distances from tree to tree, but can also pluck untended eggs or baby birds out of nests.

Widespread in South American forests, the sulfur-breasted toucan lives in small parties in the treetops.

Like all toucans, Brazil's toco toucan has a bill almost as big as its body.

223

PASSERINES

A USEFUL STARTING POINT in getting to know birds is to think of them as either passerines or non-passerines. Most birds are passerines, or perching birds. Despite their great range of shapes and sizes, they show much less diversity than all the rest of the bird groups. Passerines are the great singers of the bird world.

The painted bunting is just one of almost 5,000 species of passerine.

Tits are common songbirds in their extensive range. Here, a mother feeds her large brood.

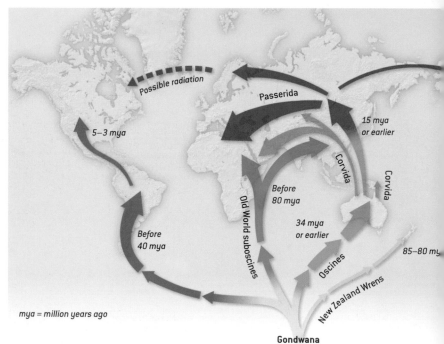

Possible radiation

Passerida

5–3 mya

15 mya or earlier

Corvida

Corvida

Before 80 mya

Old World suboscines

Before 40 mya

34 mya or earlier

Oscines

85–80 mya

New Zealand Wrens

mya = million years ago

Gondwana

PERCHING BIRDS

CLASS	Aves
ORDER	Passeriformes
FAMILIES	96
GENERA	1,218
SPECIES	5,754

Passerines—perching birds—are by far the largest order of birds. With nearly 100 families and more than 5,700 species, they make up about 60 percent of birds.

Arising some 85–80 million years ago on the southern supercontinent Gondwana, they have proven to be remarkably adaptable and have reached every continent except Antarctica. They have exploited more niches in more habitats than any other order of birds. Passerines are distinguished by their size (most are small); specialized feet for perching; and complex, muscled voice box. Being small has energetic and environmental advantages; their feet can perform many functions in many situations; and their voice boxes can sing, allowing them to communicate and mark territory easily.

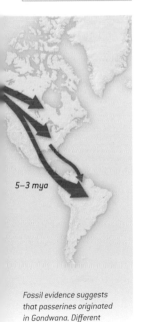

5–3 mya

Fossil evidence suggests that passerines originated in Gondwana. Different groups moved to the Old World and the New World.

Male raggiana birds-of-paradise are noted for their ornate plumage and courtship displays.

BROADBILLS

The 14 species of broadbills are very colorful. They are chunky birds with broad heads and short legs and, as their name suggests, they have broad, flattened bills.

Broadbills are confined to tropical forests in Africa, Southeast Asia and the Philippines.

Broadbills are small birds of the tropical forests. Most species are gregarious and move about the forest in small flocks. In Malaysia, the long-tailed broadbill has been seen in flocks of up to 20 in association with "bird waves" of more than 100 birds of seven or eight species.

CLASS	Aves
ORDER	Passeriformes
FAMILY	Eurylaimidae
GENERA	9
SPECIES	14

Although most broadbills are mainly insect eaters, hawking aerial insects in the lower canopy like clumsy flycatchers or catching them on the ground, they will also take small lizards and frogs. The diet of the green broadbills is predominantly soft fruits and buds.

The banded broadbill of Southeast Asia has a loud trilling call. This enables birds to stay in contact with each other in their forest habitat.

The green broadbill is a dazzling, small bird of Southeast Asian rain forests. Well camouflaged, it catches insects in the middle layers of foliage.

The blue-winged pitta is an Asian and Southeast Asian species. This brightly colored bird feeds on insects, larvae, crustaceans and snails.

PITTAS

Despite their brilliant plumage, pittas are rarely seen. They are shy birds of the forests and will quietly move into the undergrowth or leaf litter if disturbed.

The 30 species of pitta inhabit parts of Africa, southern Asia, Southeast Asia and New Guinea.

These beautiful birds resemble thrushes—indeed they are sometimes called jewel thrushes. They are medium-sized, stocky birds with strong legs, long feet and stout, slightly curved bills. Brilliantly colored, they hop among the litter of the forest floor in search of earthworms, snails and insects, probing the leaves and soil with their bill. When disturbed, they prefer to walk or run rather than fly. Their domed nests, built near or on the ground, resemble piles of debris. Both parents incubate the eggs and care for the chicks. All give loud, double whistle calls. The sexes generally look alike.

CLASS	Aves
ORDER	Passeriformes
FAMILY	Pittidae
GENUS	Pitta
SPECIES	30

The banded pitta feeds quietly on the floor of the rain forest and seldom calls.

The Indian pitta, as its name suggests, is the only pitta to inhabit the Indian subcontinent.

MANAKINS

Manakins are small birds of lowland forests of South and Central America. Most females have green or olive plumage, while the males are generally brightly colored.

Manakins are found from southern Mexico, through Central America to subtropical South America.

There are 48 species of these compact, stubby birds. Their tails are short and their wings broad and rounded. Most are forest and woodland birds that are at home in the humid tropical lowlands. They feed in the understory on fruit and berries and, sometimes, insects.

CLASS	Aves
ORDER	Passeriformes
FAMILY	Pipridae
GENERA	13
SPECIES	48

Many manakins have spectacular courtship rituals. Males clear display courts on the ground. There, they execute astonishing jumps while the wings make loud whirring and snapping sounds. Females visit males at their courts and dance with them before mating. The female builds the nest, incubates the eggs and cares for the chicks alone, since most manakins do not form stable pairs.

During courtship, the male wire-tailed manakin brushes the female's throat with the wirelike tips of his tail feathers.

The juvenile white-collared manakin blends into the foliage. Adult males have bold black, white and yellow plumage.

The blue manakin is a forest bird of southern Brazil. The male boasts a bright red crown with brilliant, glossy blue and black plumage.

The male Andean cock-of-the-rock
has a large red or orange crest;
the female is much less colorful.

COTINGAS

Cotingas are a family of 96 species of small to mid-sized birds that inhabit the treetops of the forests of Central America and tropical South America.

Some cotingas have very restricted habitats within the family's range of Mexico to South America.

Males of many species, such as the cock-of-the-rocks, are brightly colored; others, such as the unbrellabirds, are ornamented with crests, beards and wattles, all of which they use in displays. The usually much duller females undertake nesting duties unaided and lay clutches of one to four, brown-blotched eggs. Males of some species, such as the plantcutters and purpletufts, wear dull, female plumage and are monogamous, sharing in nesting duties. The aptly named bellbirds have a distinctive bell-like call that resonates through the forest.

Diet is diverse, some species eating fruit—for which they have large mouths to swallow items whole—and others, insects—which they catch by sallying in the forest canopy.

CLASS	Aves
ORDER	Passeriformes
FAMILY	Cotingidae
GENERA	33
SPECIES	96

Groups of bell miners live in open forest and woodland in eastern Australia. They drive all other birds away from their territory to protect their favored insect prey, psyllids.

TYRANT FLYCATCHERS

This New World family ranges from North America through Central and South America.

This family includes not only the tyrant flycatchers but also birds commonly known as phoebes, elaenias, kingbirds, flatbills and wood-peewees.

Tyrant flycatchers are small to medium-sized birds. The sexes look alike, generally with inconspicuous plumage that is a mixture of greens, browns, yellows and white. The males of several species are adorned with crests.

CLASS	Aves
ORDER	Passeriformes
FAMILY	Tyrannidae
GENERA	98
SPECIES	400

Most flycatchers, as their name suggests, eat insects. Each of the 400 species employs a different combination of prey size, habitat, vegetation type, foraging position and capture technique. Ornithologists believe that it is this ability to finely divide the available resources, coupled with the fact that the New World tropics provide birds with rich and diverse resources to exploit, that gave rise to this large family.

Unusually for flycatchers, the male vermillion flycatcher is bright red and the female is dull gray-brown with white underparts.

The great kiskadee is one of the most conspicuous tyrant flycatchers of tropical America.

The eared pygmy tyrant is one of the smallest in this family. The black ear patch gives the bird its name.

White throats and underparts distinguish the bicolored antbird. Like other antbirds, it follows army ants in search of food.

ANTBIRDS

Antbirds are a large family of more than 200 species, found across subtropical and tropical Central and South America, from Mexico to Argentina.

Antbirds are variously known as antshrikes, antwrens, antvireos, fire-eyes, bare-eyes and bushbirds. They are so called because they follow columns of army ants. This is one of their two main feeding strategies—finding invertebrate food flushed out by the swarming marauders. The other is to join mixed flocks of foraging birds, again to exploit prey disturbed by the noise and movement.

Each pair holds to a permanent territory—antbirds are monogamous, mate for life, and the sexes share all nesting duties. They build cup-shaped nests of vegetable matter in undergrowth and the female lays two or three white to buff eggs that are marked in red-browns and dusky tones.

The Amazon rain forest is home to the greatest diversity of antbirds. Most are forest dwellers.

CLASS	Aves
ORDER	Passeriformes
FAMILY	Thamnophilidae
GENERA	46
SPECIES	206

Antbirds are generally small and inconspicuous birds. They may flock together in search of food.

The white-faced antbird waits above a swarm of army ants, ready to pounce on any other insects they disturb.

OVENBIRDS

Ovenbirds are a large family of small birds species found in Central and South America. The ovenbird of North America is a rather distant relation.

Ovenbirds are named for their habit of building a dome-shaped nest with a side entrance resembling a Dutch oven; yet as a family they are unrivaled for the variety of nests that they make, from holes in trees and burrows in the ground, to cups and domes of plant matter in vegetation as well. All are rather small, brownish birds and most eat insects and snails. Monogamous, both sexes share all nesting duties and many roost in their nests when not breeding. Females lay plain white eggs.

CLASS	Aves
ORDER	Passeriformes
FAMILY	Furnariidae
GENERA	55
SPECIES	236

The rufous hornero builds a complex oven-like mud nest, prominently placed on a branch, rock, post or city building.

Ovenbirds forage in forest and woodland. They often search for invertebrates on the ground among fallen leaves.

Like others in this family, the cocoa woodcreeper has a long, stiff tail to help it balance on tree trunks, and strong claws for gripping bark.

WOODCREEPERS

Most woodcreepers are forest birds of Central and South America. Up to 19 species live in the Amazon rain forest.

Woodcreepers inhabit the rain forests of Central and South America. Many have restricted habitats.

The woodcreepers are tree-climbing relatives of the ovenbirds. Small and brown with streaks or bars, they have thin, straight or curved bills—good for probing trunks and branches for insects. Like antbirds, they are sometimes found in flocks attacking swarms of army ants. Their spine-tipped tails are rigid and can be used as a prop when the bird is climbing a tree. Their feet are also adapted for climbing—the front toes have strong claws. These birds may be monogamous or polygamous. When they are polygamous, females nest alone in tree holes. Eggs are plain white, in clutches of two to three.

CLASS	Aves
ORDER	Passeriformes
FAMILY	Dendrocolaptidae
GENERA	13
SPECIES	50

The long, thin, decurved bill is the distinguishing feature of the red-billed scythebill. This helps it pluck food from leaves of tree trunks.

LYREBIRDS

For those lucky enough to witness one, lyrebird displays are unforgettable—the male's tail is fanned, thrown forward and vibrated while the bird dances and sings.

Lyrebirds are confined to a belt of eucalypt and temperate rain forest along the east coast of Australia.

Lyrebirds are superb mimics and up to 80 percent of a male's song may be mimicry of other birds—occasionally it may even mimic barking dogs. Males defend their territories by chasing intruders, singing or displaying on earth mounds, which they have constructed throughout their territories.

They are pheasant-sized birds, with brown to reddish plumage, long, powerful legs, and a long tail with modified feathers; the outer two feathers in the superb lyrebird are shaped like a Greek lyre, hence the name. They are fast, agile runners when danger appears. They rarely perch in trees except to roost, ascending by jumping from branch to branch, and gliding down.

CLASS	Aves
ORDER	Passeriformes
FAMILY	Menuridae
GENUS	Menura
SPECIES	2

To attract a mate, a male superb lyrebird spreads his tail into a spectacular fan, and starts to sing and dance.

The male lyrebird mates with a number of females attracted by his display. The female builds a domed nest and incubates the single egg.

The male satin bowerbird has glossy blue-black plumage, blue eyes and a yellow bill; the female is smaller, with olive green plumage.

BOWERBIRDS

Bowerbirds inhabit rain forest, eucalypt forest and dry shrubland. Their diet consists mainly of fruit but may also include insects and nectar.

There are 18 species of bowerbird. All are endemic to New Guinea and north, central and eastern Australia

Bowerbirds are best known for their unique courtship behavior, where males build a shelter, or bower, and decorate it to attract a mate. Females build a nest of leaves or ferns on top of a foundation of sticks. They lay one or two eggs, which hatch after 19 to 24 days. Females raise their young alone. Some bowerbirds are brilliant mimics. Australia's satin bowerbirds often mimic other local species as part of their courtship display while other species have been observed imitating human voices. While the three species of catbird in this family are monogamous, all other male bowerbirds are polygamous.

CLASS	Aves
ORDER	Passeriformes
FAMILY	Ptilonorhynchidae
GENERA	8
SPECIES	18

Female satin bowerbirds are dull in color to blend in with the forest and the foliage around her nest.

Females visit three or four bowers and mate with males whose bowers are solidly built and elaborately decorated.

BOWER POWER

Bowerbirds are noted for their displays. But, unlike birds-of-paradise, the emphasis is not on spectacular plumage, but on the "bower" constructed by the male.

The great bowerbird, like the satin bowerbird, builds an avenue bower of twigs. It displays shells, bones, glass and other treasures.

Bowerbirds are the master builders of the avian world. The males build bowers, which are ornamental platforms, towers or avenues of sticks. The bowers are not nests; they are more like bachelor pads, where the male performs to attract as many females as possible. Bowers are often decorated with particular colors or objects, and are sometimes painted, using a brush made of leaves or twigs. Many early ornithologists refused to believe that birds could be responsible for building such elaborate structures. Male bowerbirds are polygamous and the females carry out nesting duties alone.

The satin bowerbird of Australia constructs a classic avenue bower. This consists of two parallel walls of sticks, with a display area in front. Some other species also build a roof.

Macgregor's bowerbird, of New Guinea's highland forests, builds a typical maypole bower. A tower of twigs and grass is arranged around the base of a small sapling.

Newton's golden bowerbird is one of the smaller bowerbirds, but the chamber it builds is one of the largest and most impressive. A display perch connects the two maypoles.

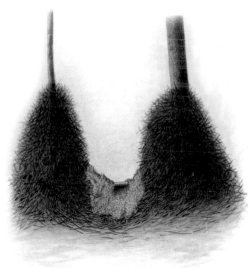

249

All fairy-wrens are insectivores, and most forage on the ground or among the underbrush. The superb fairy-wren is a tiny but brilliant species.

FAIRY-WRENS

Fairy-wrens are cock-tailed undergrowth foragers.
Females are the matriarchs of fairy-wren social groups,
guarded by males which help year their young.

*This family is confined to Australia,
New Zealand, and New Guinea
and its adjacent islands.*

The similarities between the fairy-wrens, grass-wrens, wren-warblers and emu-wrens of Australia and New Guinea and the wrens of the Northern Hemisphere are that they are all small and all cock their tails.

CLASS	Aves
ORDER	Passeriformes
FAMILY	Maluridae
GENERA	5
SPECIES	28

Male fairy-wrens are among the jewels of the Australian bush—these tiny creatures are arrayed in stunning combinations of turquoise, red, black and white. Their mates are more somber. Although the emu-wrens, which derive their name from sparse emulike tail feathers, have blue bibs, and some of the secretive grass-wrens have bold black and chestnut colors, the design is for camouflage rather than display.

*Females (on the right) are the
matriarchs of fairy-wren social
groups. Males guard the territory
and help rear the chicks.*

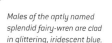

*Males of the aptly named
splendid fairy-wren are clad
in glittering, iridescent blue.*

HONEYEATERS

Honeyeaters are the largest bird family in Australasia. Living in trees and shrubbery, they are small to mid-sized gray and green birds and the sexes are usually alike.

The honeyeaters are birds of Australasia; most species are found in Australia and New Guinea.

Curved bills and brush-tipped tongues allow them to pursue different foods—nectar, fruit and insects—as opportunities offer. Species more dependent on nectar tend to be nomadic in their search for flowering plants. Many honeyeaters congregate at food sources, where they create aggressive peck-orders. Though monogamous, they often mate only for breeding. Females carry out most nesting duties, building cup-nests slung in foliage. Their clutches of one to five eggs are usually pale pink with red and dusky spots.

CLASS	Aves
ORDER	Passeriformes
FAMILY	Meliphagidae
GENERA	44
SPECIES	174

The mao of Samoa is a large, endangered honeyeater. Slash-and-burn farming and introduced non-native trees have threatened its forest habitat.

The regent honeyeater is a bird of the eucalypt forests. Like the spinebill, it is a nectar eater.

The eastern spinebill is abundant in thickets of flowering shrubs. It has a long, slender bill.

New Holland honeyeaters have prominent yellow edges around the tail feathers. The male is largely black-toned; females and juveniles are duller.

The female varied triller, seen here, is not as boldly marked as the male in his bold breeding plumage. The birds form monogamous pairs.

CUCKOOSHRIKES

Cuckooshrikes are so called because of their hard-shafted yet loosely attached rump feathers, which are similar to those of Old World cuckoos, and their shrikelike bills.

Cuckooshrikes range through Africa, Asia and the Pacific. Many species are restricted to small islands.

Cuckooshrikes are moderately large, gray or blackish and white, and generally barred. Males and females are similar in appearance. Their bill is relatively heavy, broad-based and hook-tipped, and they have short legs. They are tree-dwelling perchers that feed on insects. Pairs build tiny saucer-shaped nests camouflaged with cobwebs on high branches. Most are secretive birds, hiding among screening foliage as they forage for insects and fruit.

CLASS	Aves
ORDER	Passeriformes
FAMILY	Campephagidae
GENERA	7
SPECIES	81

Among the cuckooshrike group are the trillers, which have blackish gray and white plumage, with some tinged a rust color; and the woodshrikes, which are gray, black and white in color. Males of many species of minivets are bright red, orange and yellow, and all females are less colorful than the males.

The barred cuckooshrike is gray with a distinctive yellow eye and black and white barred belly. It is a partial migrant, moving in search of fruit.

The pied triller lives in India, Southeast Asia and the Philippines. It has adapted to urban conditions, and can be found in parks and gardens.

VIREOS

Vireos are a group of around 50 small to medium-sized birds endemic to the Americas. They appear to be related to the crows and shrikes.

Vireos are distributed through the Americas. Many migrate from North to South America in winter.

They are mostly dull-colored and greenish; the sexes rarely differ. All are arboreal, the typical vireos gleaning for insects, the brighter shrike-vireos taking fruit, and the peppershrikes both. The black-capped vireo joins mixed species feeding flocks, picking up insect prey disturbed by other birds. They sing loudly and compulsively. Vireos build deep, cup-shaped nests from fine grass, spider's silk and strips of bark and suspend them by their rims in branch forks at various heights in trees or shrubs.

CLASS	Aves
ORDER	Passeriformes
FAMILY	Vireonidae
GENERA	4
SPECIES	52

The males are often persistent singers. Their songs range from simple, monotonous calls to the more mellow warblings of the peppershrikes.

Vireos build their nests at various heights in trees or shrubs, suspending them by their rims in branch forks.

The warbling vireo is a widely distributed woodland bird, with a long warbling song.

The white-eyed vireo forages for arthropods in low scrub. They sing all year, not just when courting, with a repetitive and unmusical call.

VANGAS

The vangas are a diverse group of songbirds found only on the island of Madagascar, a long isolated island of diverse habitats the size of California.

Vangas are endemic to Madagascar. They have diversified to inhabit a variety of habitats on the island.

Vangas are the tree shrikes of Madagascar, but their bills have diversified from thickened and hooked to slender and curved, for catching insects on the wing, probing into crevices, hop-gleaning up trunks, and grabbing small amphibians and reptiles. Rough cup-nests are placed in an upright fork or woven on to horizontal branches.

CLASS	Aves
ORDER	Passeriformes
FAMILY	Vangidae
GENERA	15
SPECIES	22

The blue vanga inhabits evergreen forests and clearings. It can be found in mixed-species flocks catching insects from bushes and in flight.

Sickle-billed vanga

Lafresnaye's vanga

Helmet vanga

Red-shouldered vanga

Blue vanga

Vangas have specialized so much that there are almost as many genera as species in this group. The 22 species of vanga all prey on invertebrates or small reptiles but, to avoid competition, have each evolved different bills to take prey of different size from different niches.

The long bill of the sickle-billed vanga is ideal for grazing invertebrates in spiny forests.

The loggerhead shrike is one of the American species. An insect eater, it prefers open country. Northern populations migrate south in winter.

SHRIKES

This family of medium-sized birds comprises three distinct groups: the helmet shrikes and the white-headed shrikes; the bush shrikes; and the "true," predatory shrikes.

The shrikes are primarily an Old World family. Only two species are found in North America.

The true shrikes are patterned in gray, chestnut, black and white, and many of the African species are pied. All have a hooked and notched bill, and almost all are territorial and solitary. Most bush shrikes are attractively colored on the underside. Helmet shrikes are characterized by feathering on the crown, which forms a brush-fronted "helmet."

From a vantage perch, true shrikes watch for prey, which they seize on the ground, and many are renowned for their habit of impaling surplus food on the thorns of bushes or barbed wire fencing. Most bush shrikes glean insects from tree limbs and foliage, while helmet shrikes roam through woodland in parties feeding in the trees.

CLASS	*Aves*
ORDER	*Passeriformes*
FAMILY	*Laniidae*
GENERA	*4*
SPECIES	*30*

The rufous-backed shrike is a true shrike of southern Asia, from Iran to New Guinea.

The red-backed shrike swoops down on its insect and small animal prey from a prominent perch.

BIRDS-OF-PARADISE

Birds-of-paradise are justly famous for their ornate plumage and their impressive displays. Males flaunt their plumes to attract the attention of the much duller females.

Birds-of-paradise are confined to Australasia. They are most abundant in New Guinea.

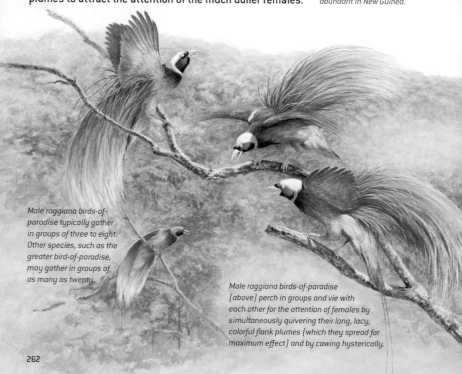

Male raggiana birds-of-paradise typically gather in groups of three to eight. Other species, such as the greater bird-of-paradise, may gather in groups of as many as twenty.

Male raggiana birds-of-paradise (above) perch in groups and vie with each other for the attention of females by simultaneously quivering their long, lacy, colorful flank plumes (which they spread for maximum effect) and by cawing hysterically.

CLASS	Aves
ORDER	Passeriformes
FAMILY	Paradisaeidae
GENERA	16
SPECIES	40

Males of different species have different courtship rituals; among the best known are those of the raggiana bird-of-paradise, in which the males congregate in courting arenas, or leks, in the forest, spreading their colorful plumes while posturing and dancing on high, bare branches. Females observe the show, mate, then leave to nest on their own.

Dull female raggiana birds-of-paradise visit the lek to observe the males' displays. Studies have shown that most females mate with the same male, presumably the one that is most dominant, judged by prowess in display.

Male Asiatic paradise flycatchers' tail feathers grow up to 12 inches (30 cm) long. This does not stop them taking turns sitting on their tiny cup nest.

MONARCH FLYCATCHERS

There are almost 90 species of these small songbirds. The family reaches its greatest diversity in the tropical rain forests of New Guinea.

The monarchs are distributed from sub-Saharan Africa, through India and Southeast Asia, to Australasia.

Rufous, black, white, blue or gray, often with iridescent highlights, are the most common plumage colors of these birds, but spectacular exceptions include the black and yellow boatbills and the paradise flycatchers, in which the males have striking, long tails that can exceed 12 inches (30 cm) in length. Monarchs have a predilection for flicking their tails and occasionally raising crests, which give many of the species a characteristically steep forehead.

CLASS	Aves
ORDER	Passeriformes
FAMILY	Monarchidae
GENERA	16
SPECIES	87

Most tropical monarchs are resident, but those breeding in temperate regions—such as some populations of the Asiatic paradise flycatcher, the black-faced monarch and the satin flycatcher of southeastern Australia— migrate to the tropics in the winter.

The spectacled monarch darts about shrubbery in Australian rain forests, fluttering its wide-tipped tail to flush out insects.

The pale-blue monarch of Indonesia builds a small cup-nest. The male is brilliant blue and the female, shown here, is duller.

CROWS AND JAYS

Crows, rooks, ravens, jays, magpies and nutcrackers make up this group. Most are big, bold and versatile songbirds; they appear in most habitats in most parts of the world.

Most are medium to large in size, with nostrils covered with bristles, and relatively long legs. Color varies from the somber black of the raven through to the brilliant reds and greens of the Asian magpies. Their nests, usually bulky cups of sticks, are built high in trees. The female alone broods her clutch of two to five dusky-spotted eggs.

They forage on the ground, probing with their strong bills to search for insects, tear meat from carcasses, harvest berries or pick up fallen seeds. Many of the smaller species forage in the forest canopy, and some harvest nuts and pine seeds, which they may hide in caches to be used later.

Members of this family are extremely widespread, occurring in all continents except Antarctica.

CLASS	Aves
ORDER	Passeriformes
FAMILY	Corvidae
GENERA	24
SPECIES	117

Rooks forage in fields and pastures of open country, probing with their large bills for insects and other prey.

From a distance, magpies look black and white, but a closer view shows green, purple and blue hues in their feathers.

266

The blue jay is a common and widespread bird of the woodlands, parks and gardens of North America.

The blue tit—active, entertaining and hardy—is a popular visitor at garden bird-feeders across Europe. Its natural habitat is temperate forests.

TITS AND CHICKADEES

Tits and chickadees are widespread, and are sometimes the most obvious small songbirds in parts of their far-flung range. Some are familiar urban dwellers.

Tits and chickadees are widely distributed in Africa, Europe, Asia, North and Central America.

Few of the 54 species exceed 5 inches (13 cm) in length. They tend to be brown, gray or green above, and paler or yellow underneath. Most have black caps, some with crests. The azure tit and the blue tit are predominantly blue above. They have short, straight bills; in many species these are slightly stubby and capable of hammering open small nuts. Those species that live in conifer forests have finer bills, probably so that they can probe into clusters of needles.

CLASS	Aves
ORDER	Passeriformes
FAMILY	Paridae
GENERA	3
SPECIES	54

They feed on a wide range of insects and seeds, although all bring insect food to their nestlings; many are seed eaters in the colder times of the year.

The tufted titmouse, the only crested member of the family, is common through eastern North America.

In winter, the coal tit (left) often joins relatives such as the great tit (right) in foraging parties in European woods.

269

SWALLOWS AND MARTINS

Swallows and martins are the songbird equivalent of swifts—streamlined and swift of wing for hawking for flying insects, and weak of foot for perching at rest.

They are small, slender birds that catch insects in mid-air, more or less sucking them up as they fly in graceful swoops and glides, usually at no great height over open ground. In some parts of the world they may be seen perched in twittering flocks along telephone lines when not feeding. They usually nest in colonies, either in holes or burrows, or attach mud nests of pellets to walls, some of them bottle-shaped. Females build the nest from mud brought by males.

The plumage of typical swallows is glossy blue-black on the upper parts, dark on the wings and tail, which is spotted with white. Most swallows and martins are migrants.

Swallows and martins are found throughout most of the world's tropical and temperate zones.

CLASS	Aves
ORDER	Passeriformes
FAMILY	Hirundinidae
GENERA	20
SPECIES	84

The male purple martin is a glossy blue-black above and below, while the female is brownish with a pale belly.

Swallows are well adapted to their long-distance migration flights, with streamlined bodies and long wings.

Reinforced, hollow wing bones make the skeleton sturdy yet light enough for flying.

Barn swallows nest in caves. They have also adapted to urban environments and nest in old buildings and on window ledges.

Long, forked tail feathers enable a swallow to regulate its speed, steer and brake quickly.

Two sets of muscles attached to the breastbone drive the wings up and down.

The song of the skylark is one of the most melodious in the world. Skylarks rely on their song, rather than colorful plumage, to attract mates.

LARKS

The 92 species of lark are widespread, except for Central and South America and parts of Australia. Not all have the vocal powers of the renowned skylark of Eurasia.

Typical larks are streaked brown over the upper parts, wings and tail, and white or buff on the underside; the breast is usually streaked with dark brown. Some have a small crest on the head. In most, the bill is slender and slightly decurved. All walk rather than hop.

Larks feed on insects and other invertebrates, seeds and grain. They build cup-shaped nests on the ground; these are sometimes exposed and sometimes sheltered at the base of a tuft of grass or under a low bush. In desert a partial canopy may be added to shield the incubating female from the heat of the sun.

This family occurs throughout temperate regions worldwide, but is more prevalent in the Old World.

CLASS	Aves
ORDER	Passeriformes
FAMILY	Alaudidae
GENERA	19
SPECIES	92

Western meadowlarks perch, raise their heads and give out their territorial display calls.

The Eurasian woodlark inhabits woodlands, heathland and open country. It forages on the ground for invertebrates and vegetable matter.

273

BULBULS

Bulbuls are common, smallish, gray or green songbirds of the Old World tropics. Many are crested and most are active, noisy, and live in either tree foliage or shrubberies.

The bulbul's natural range includes sub-Saharan Africa, Japan, and southern and Southeast Asia.

Rounded wings and long, squarish-tipped tails give them good maneuverability and strong flight. Bills are short and slender, slightly hooked, and surrounded by bristles; they are used to pick fruit and pounce on insects. Bulbuls have adapted to both open woodlands and forests. Most species forage in foliage but those in open habitats have become specialized ground feeders.

CLASS	*Aves*
ORDER	*Passeriformes*
FAMILY	*Pycnonotidae*
GENERA	*20*
SPECIES	*130*

Bulbuls are monogamous and, although gregarious in roaming bands when not breeding, pairs defend nest territory. The sexes look alike and both share nesting duties. They build rough, cup-shaped nests that are usually perched, but sometimes suspended, in low trees and shrubs.

The red-vented bulbul lives in gardens and scrub from Pakistan and India to southwest China.

Bulbuls feed on fruit, although they will also eat insects. Most, like this red-eyed bulbul, are loud and gregarious birds.

Most species of bulbuls, like this Himalayan bulbul, have rather dull plumage of browns and olives. Many have a small crest.

The blue-winged warbler forages constantly in dense foliage, pausing to sing. It breeds in North America and winters in Central America.

OLD WORLD WARBLERS

The core Old World warblers are small, sweet-voiced birds of woods and grassy fields. Many breed in high latitudes and migrate to the tropics for winter.

Old World warblers are widely distributed. Most reside in Africa; many others migrate to winter there.

Their bills are straight, narrow and mostly short; their navigation has a strong genetic component. There are four subfamilies: the west Pacific grassbirds; the Afro-Eurasian bush and reed warblers; the Afro-Asian leaf warblers; and the typical Eurasian warblers. All eat insects and forage unobtrusively by hop-gleaning in foliage and herbage, often alone. Both sexes usually share nesting duties, building cup-shaped nests of fiber in deep foliage or grass tussocks and reeds. They brood clutches of three to six, white to buff, usually spotted eggs.

CLASS	Aves
ORDER	Passeriformes
FAMILY	Sylviidae
GENERA	48
SPECIES	265

Like other reed warblers, the great reed warbler lives in thick reedbeds. It has a rich and varied song.

The blackburnian warbler is a forest dweller. It breeds in North America and migrates to Central and South America for winter.

THE YELLOW WARBLER'S YEAR

One of the most widespread warblers in North America, the yellow warbler nests in woodlands, orchards, and groves of willows and alders.

This warbler is well named, the male's face and underparts being bright yellow. The female is duller than the male but is still yellowish overall, her head and upper parts washed with olive.

The breeding cycles of songbirds are relatively brief. Most of them take only a week or two to find a mate; four or five days to build a nest; five to seven days to lay eggs, depending on the clutch size; and ten to 15 days for incubation. Their young become fledglings between ten and 21 days.

AUGUST
Depart breeding ground

SEPTEMBER
Return to Costa Ric

JULY
Molt

JUNE
Young depart nest

MAY
Sing to attract mate
Build nest
Lay and incubate eggs

Breeding males have the brightest plumage of this species. They often call from near the tops of trees to announce their territory.

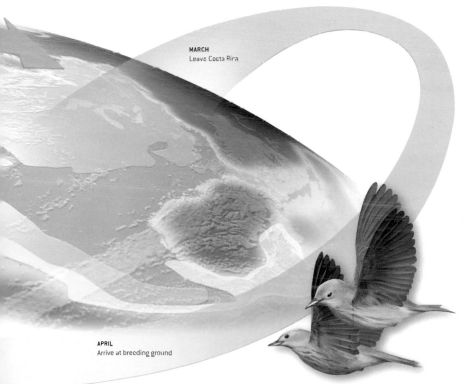

MARCH
Leave Costa Rica

APRIL
Arrive at breeding ground

The red-billed leiothrix is found in forests in India, Burma, the Himalayas and southen China. Often kept as a pet, it has been introduced to Hawaii.

BABBLERS

Afro-Eurasian babblers are widely distributed, gregarious chatterboxes of undergrowth, scrub and foliage; only the wren-tit is found on the west coast of the United States.

Babblers are largely Old World birds, found in Africa, Europe and Asia. Most species are in Southeast Asia.

Protectively toned in browns and grays, they are mostly short-winged and stout-legged and use their legs to hold prey. None are long-distance migrants. They hop actively about, in and out of water to bathe, among ground foliage, probing for seeds and small invertebrates—often ants. Bill form varies in adaptation to diet, and some species with long-curved bills and brush-tipped tongues take nectar. Babblers work in small flocks, feeding, resting and cluster-roosting together. Both sexes and often helpers build mostly cup-shaped nests of fiber, secreted in shrubs. Eggs vary from white to blue and plain to spotted brown, according to species.

CLASS	Aves
ORDER	Passeriformes
FAMILY	Timaliidae
GENERA	55
SPECIES	280

Like the other scimitar babblers of Southeast Asia and India, the coral-billed scimitar babbler forages for invertebrates in forest leaf-litter.

WRENS

Wrens are small, drab, brown birds that usually inhabit undergrowth or very low vegetation. They are active and have high-pitched, vigorous songs.

Except for one Eurasian species, wrens are confined to the New World. Most species occur near the tropics.

Most wrens are smallish birds, the largest being the cactus wren, about 8.5 inches (22 cm) long. They have short, rounded wings and are not strong fliers. All are grayish or brownish in color, many heavily streaked with black, and some have white eye-stripes or white throats. Many wrens have powerful voices and some are highly musical. They are insect eaters; some also eat seeds.

CLASS	Aves
ORDER	Passeriformes
FAMILY	Troglodytidae
GENERA	17
SPECIES	77

The wrens are a New World family, except for the winter wren, which is also found in Eurasia, where it is known simply as the wren. Most wren species occur in South and Central America. Nine species breed in North America.

Male marsh wrens lead prospective mates to their nests with soft singing and wing fluttering.

The winter wren is a common Northern Hemisphere garden bird. Small with dull plumage, it is known for posturing with a bobbing head and cocked tail.

America's mockingbird is a prodigious mimic—the more calls a male can make, the greater are its chances of attracting a mate.

MOCKINGBIRDS AND THRASHERS

Mockingbirds and their allies are thrushlike birds of the New World. The family includes 34 species of mockingbirds, catbirds, mocking-thrush, tremblers and thrashers.

This family is found from southern Canada through North and Central America to South America.

They are sturdy-legged terrestrial or low-vegetation birds, with strong downcurved bills, short wings and long tails. Almost all species are gray or brown, but many have lovely patterns to distinguish them. The family is noted for its beautiful singers and mimics. The northern mockingbird may imitate as many as 20 local bird species. All species are strongly territorial; mockingbirds will aggressively attack transgressors. Most species forage on the ground, taking terrestrial invertebrates, which they find by using their downcurved bill to dig in the soil or search under surface debris. They also eat small fruit.

CLASS	Aves
ORDER	Passeriformes
FAMILY	Mimidae
GENERA	12
SPECIES	34

The brown thrasher is a common bird of North America, but is inconspicuous because of its brownish-gray plumage.

The gray catbird is named for its catlike, mewing call. It is one of the smallest birds in the family but undertakes a lengthy annual migration.

STARLINGS

Starlings are Old World birds, with strongest representation in hotter climates. A number have glossy black plumage, but many are brilliantly colored.

This family is native to the Old World but the common starling has been widely introduced elsewhere.

These are small to medium-sized birds with strong bills and legs. Most species are gregarious and many roost in flocks. The common starling, one of the most widespread and widely recognized of all birds, is typical of the family. It is a stumpy, short-tailed bird with a confident strut and an alert manner. The 35 African species of starling include some beautiful birds with glossy, iridescent plumage, often featuring patches of vivid violet, green, orange and blue. The mynahs of India are dull brown, with patches of naked yellow skin on the head and white flashes in the wing. Most starlings are insect eaters, although some forest-dwellers take fruits.

CLASS	Aves
ORDER	Passeriformes
FAMILY	Sturnidae
GENERA	25
SPECIES	115

The superb glossy starling of East Africa is a frequent visitor to campsites and picnic grounds.

The common starling is a familiar bird, as it has adapted to urban habitats. It forages where it can.

The red-billed oxpecker of Africa feeds on parasites on large mammals, such as impala. It also takes blood from wounds, and hair to use as nest lining.

The fieldfare is one of the larger thrushes, common in much of northern Europe. In winter, huge flocks migrate south to feed on invertebrates.

THRUSHES

The 165 species of thrush are widespread except for parts of Australia and New Zealand. The songs of some species are among the most beautiful of all bird songs.

Thrushes are found everywhere except for the high Arctic, Antarctica and parts of Australasia.

The birds in this group range from the forest rock-thrush, at 0.75 oz (21 g), to the blue whistling-thrush at 7.5 oz (178 g). Thrushes are mid-sized, dull-colored songbirds that forage by hop-search, mainly on the ground. They peck and shuffle about for a variety of invertebrate food and their stout legs characteristically lack scaling. All are monogamous and solitary. Males aggressively defend breeding territory by singing from vantage perches and by physical attack. Females carry out nest-building, constructing sturdy, cup-shaped nests, sometimes bound with mud, in branch forks or in rock crevices. They also brood their spotted, cream to blue eggs unaided. Both parents feed the young.

CLASS	Aves
ORDER	Passeriformes
FAMILY	Turdidae
GENERA	24
SPECIES	165

The rich song of the white-rumped shama rivals that of the more famous nightingale.

Despite its dull plumage, the blackbird has a musical, warbling call. It is a common ground forager.

OLD WORLD CHATS AND FLYCATCHERS

Old World chats and flycatchers are small insect eaters that forage in woodlands and forests. They capture prey on the wing, picking it off from trees or in mid-air.

The flycatchers and chats are widely distributed in the Old World, from Europe to New Guinea.

Their short, narrow bills are broadened at the base and surrounded by short bristles for protection. Few feed on the ground or in grassland. Most species in the boreal temperate zone are migratory, wintering in the tropics. Males, commonly the brighter colored sex, defend breeding territory while females build cup-nests of fiber and incubate alone, brooding large clutches of two to eight blue-green eggs. Both parents rear the young.

CLASS	Aves
ORDER	Passeriformes
FAMILY	Muscicapidae
GENERA	48
SPECIES	275

Fifteen flycatchers are listed as threatened, of which ten are vulnerable, four are endangered and one critical. The critical species is Rück's blue flycatcher from the diminishing rain forests of north Sumatra.

The rufous-bellied niltava is a migrant of forest undergrowth.

The tiny male bluethroat has a distinctive blue bib with bands of orange, black and white across the breast.

European robins—iconic birds of the continent—select one or more song perches that they use for their territorial or courting singing.

The white-bellied sunbird of southern Africa feeds on nectar with its downcurved bill. It collects spiderweb to use with grass and leaves to make a nest.

SUNBIRDS

Sunbirds and spiderhunters are the Old World equivalent of hummingbirds, with long downcurved bills and brush-tipped, tubed and protrucible tongues

Sunbirds are distributed from sub-Saharan Africa through southern Asia to Melanesia and Australia.

The smallest bird in the family is the tiny black-bellied sunbird, weighing in at 0.2 oz (5 g); the largest is the spectacled spiderhunter at 1.6 oz (45 g) Sunbirds are solitary when foraging, mostly for nectar although they will also take insects. Dull, olive-plumaged females build long, domed nests hung by a stem or sewn to the undersides of leaves. Females also brood their clutches of two to three bluish white, gray, and brownish marked eggs alone. Males, usually brilliantly plumaged in metallic colors, help with young Spiderhunters are usually larger than the sunbirds and both sexes have drab brown plumage.

CLASS	Aves
ORDER	Passeriformes
FAMILY	Nectariniidae
GENERA	16
SPECIES	127

The female brown-throated sunbird has dull plumage, whereas the male is brilliant green and purple above and yellow below.

WEAVERS

The weavers are a largely African family of 108 species. They are small and gregarious seed eaters, and are named for their elaborate woven nests.

Weavers are found in sub-Saharan Africa, south and Southeast Asia. A few inhabit Indian Ocean islands.

CLASS	Aves
ORDER	Passeriformes
FAMILY	Ploceidae
GENERA	11
SPECIES	108

The family is subdivided into buffalo-weavers, sparrow-weavers and true weavers (which include bishops and widow birds). Bishops are named for the hood of red or yellow in the males' breeding plumage. Some long-tailed species are called "widows" after the train or tail, as in a widow's mourning veil. Colonies of hundreds of true weaver nests are conspicuous in the African landscape. Most males have brightly colored plumage, although some species are black. Females are mainly brown.

Some forest-dwelling weavers eat insects, but the majority of species feed on grass seeds, though they may feed insects to their young.

Red bishops are common in southern Africa. Males don red and black only for breeding.

The male long-tailed widowbird, seen here in breeding plumage, molts to short-tailed, brown plumage when breeding is finished.

The male black-headed weaver stitches strips of vegetation together to make a roofed basket. He ties knots, using grasses, to make the nest secure. Weavers nest in colonies, although the females tend the eggs and raise the young alone.

The Gouldian finch was once widespread across northern Australia. It is a popular cage bird and its numbers have declined in the wild.

WAXBILLS AND GRASSFINCHES

Waxbills and grassfinches, the smallest of all finches, are brilliantly colored in reds, blues, greens and yellows. They feed mainly on seeds, often in flocks.

These birds are found in south Asia, sub-Saharan Africa, Madagascar, Australia and the southwest Pacific.

Like other finches, they have a crop and muscular stomach for storing and grinding food. Some species also take insects, such as ants and termites. Males court by hopping about an intended mate, holding a feather or piece of grass in the bill, and singing. Both sexes share nesting duties. They build rough, domed nests of stems and fiber in shrubberies and incubate clutches of four to six plain, white eggs. Dormitory nests are built for sleeping. Nestlings have luminous mouth-spots that signpost feeding parents to their mouths. Adults have the rare ability to regurgitate whole crop contents in a single movement.

CLASS	Aves
ORDER	Passeriformes
FAMILY	Estrididae
GENERA	26
SPECIES	130

During the dry season, the melba finch uses its sharp bill to dig into termite nests.

The black-cheeked waxbill is a bird of dry grasslands and acacia scrub in parts of sub-Saharan Africa.

THE SONG OF THE ZEBRA FINCH

Zebra finches, widespread throughout the inland of Australia and easily kept in captivity, are among the best studied of all songbirds.

The male zebra finch has a shrill and persistent song. Its black and white bands give it its common name.

To make their songs heard far afield, birds may sing from the highest perches available. This is also one reason that many species prefer to sing in the morning, when the clear air helps carry the sound farther. Birds can produce sounds with higher frequencies than the human voice.

The zebra finch, primarily a seed eater, feeds on insects and termites if seeds are in short supply. It flocks around waterholes.

Male zebra finches (above left) sing far more loudly when other birds are present, in order to prompt females (far left) to respond to their advances and to ward off other males.

Most male songbirds can sing two or more different songs. Female zebra finches have been shown to consistently prefer males with more complex songs.

Songs help coordinate the reproductive cycles of mates. They can prompt females to ovulate, build nests and lay eggs.

Wagtails, such as this gray wagtail, are patterned in yellow, gray and white, in contrast to the brownish, black-streaked pipits.

PIPITS AND WAGTAILS

Pipits and wagtails are small, slender, long-tailed insectivores. They run here and there over the ground to pick up food, then stop and wag the tail up and down.

Pipits and wagtails are widespread, although fewer species are found in North America.

Pipits have streaky plumage, long hind claws and long tails. Wagtails are similar in form but with even longer tails. Most species are found near watery habitats. Some species are black, white and gray; others have yellow in their plumage.

Their flight is swift and undulating, and many species are migratory. They congregate in loose groups then, but when breeding, they break up into solitary pairs. Male and female court in song-flights, then either both, or the female alone, build a cup-nest of fiber on the ground or in a rock crevice. They incubate a clutch of between two to seven whitish eggs that have gray markings.

CLASS	Aves
ORDER	Passeriformes
FAMILY	Motacillidae
GENERA	5
SPECIES	64

Breeding in Europe and western and central Asia, the tree pipit winters in Africa and southern Asia.

The white wagtail is widespread. The pattern of its plumage varies across its range.

FINCHES

True finches have short, cone-shaped bills for picking up and husking small seeds. Bill shapes differ according to the types of seed that are eaten.

Finches are widespread. Species can be found on all continents except Antarctica and Australia.

Seeds are wedged into a groove in the palate, cracked by the heavily muscled lower bill, then husked by manipulation of the tongue. Feeding in shrubbery or trees, finches flock after breeding, but nest in pairs. Males, many brilliantly colored, display in song-flights over nesting space. Females build neat,

CLASS	Aves
ORDER	Passeriformes
FAMILY	Fringillidae
GENERA	42
SPECIES	168

cup-shaped nests in trees or shrubs. Eggs are bluish white, spotted red-black. These tiny birds are popular as pets because of their often brilliant plumage and attractive songs.

The male chaffinch is brightly colored and handsomely plumed. It is a common bird in European parks and gardens.

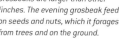

Grosbeaks are larger than other finches. The evening grosbeak feeds on seeds and nuts, which it forages from trees and on the ground.

The breeding male American goldfinch takes on a bright yellow hue—hence its common name of wild canary. Both sexes are much duller in winter.

The common yellowthroat is widely distributed through North and Central America. The male, shown here, has a black face mask.

NEW WORLD WARBLERS

The 116 species of New World warbler are small insect eaters. They don yellow or sometimes reddish plumage patterns when breeding—males more than females.

Widely distributed through North America to South America, this group is not related to Old World warblers.

Their short, slender bills are adapted to gleaning, but some have broader, bristled bills and catch prey on the wing. Many are migratory. Females build cup-nests and brood alone.

About half these warblers are migratory, wintering in Central and South America. They have habituated to urban environments and many species are common in city parks and gardens.

CLASS	Aves
ORDER	Passeriformes
FAMILY	Parulidae
GENERA	26
SPECIES	116

In the orange-crowned warbler (top) sexual differences in breeding plumage hardly exist; in the magnolia warbler (bottom right), they are slight but clear; and in the American redstart (bottom left), they are striking.

NEW WORLD BLACKBIRDS

New World blackbirds are more diverse in form and habits than any other family of birds. Most species are found in the tropics.

New World blackbirds are distributed through North America to South America and the West Indies.

In form, they range from the small, finchlike bobolink, through the multicolored New World orioles to large, black, crowlike grackles, cowbirds and oropendolas. Males are commonly much larger and more brightly colored than females. The group includes seed eaters, fruit eaters and insect eaters, with variable bills to match their feeding styles. Some feed in trees and others, such as the meadowlarks, on the ground where they resemble Old World pipits. Bills are pointed and un-notched, and grackles have a special ridge in the palate that works like a can opener to shell acorns.

CLASS	Aves
ORDER	Passeriformes
FAMILY	Icteridae
GENERA	26
SPECIES	98

Up to 40 million brown-headed cowbirds live in the woodlands, grasslands or gardens of North America.

Large and noisy roosts of the great-tailed grackle are typical of towns and villages in Mexico and Central America.

The female spot-breasted oriole, like most tropical orioles, is as bright as the male. She also sings, though her call is not as loud as the male's.

The snow bunting breeds in the Arctic circle in summer. The male, shown here, arrives earlier than the female. Nests are made in deep rock crevices.

BUNTINGS AND AMERICAN SPARROWS

Buntings and American sparrows are a large group—308 species—of small, finchlike birds in brown, dusky-streaked plumage, the males usually brighter than females.

Their stout bills are adapted to seed-eating and have a humped palate against which seeds can be cracked for shelling. Although insects are minor in the adult diet, they are fed to protein-needy nestlings. Like other finches, buntings congregate to feed and roost in large flocks when not breeding but split into territory-holding pairs to nest. Most species are monogamous, and males chase their mates in headlong flights in the lead-up to nesting. Females bear the brunt of nesting duties, with some help from males. They build cup-shaped, or in the tropics, domed nests in crevices and cavities on the ground or in low rock faces and shrubberies.

These birds are abundantly distributed except for Madagascar, Indonesia and Australasia.

CLASS	Aves
ORDER	Passeriformes
FAMILY	Emberizidae
GENERA	73
SPECIES	308

The corn bunting's song starts with a few, slow chipping notes and ends in a fast jingle.

Many white-crowned sparrows breed in northern Canada and Alaska, but in winter move south into the US, where they forage in large flocks.

TANAGERS AND HONEYCREEPERS

The 271 species of tanagers and honeycreepers, small to medium in size, are centered in the northern Andes. This group includes some of the most colorful of all birds.

Tanangers and honeycreepers are birds of the New World, ranging through North and South America.

Compensating for poor song, their plumage vies with the birds-of-paradise and cotingas as the most brilliant passerines. Males are usually more brightly colored than females. Shortish-tailed and long-legged, they live mostly in trees and shrubs, using bills of diverse form to take various foods. Some have finchlike bills for seed-eating; many have straight, narrow bills to pick fruit or catch insects; and others have slender, curved bills for rifling nectar from flowers. They roost in trees and bushes. Both sexes, or the female alone, construct the nest, usually a cup of fiber or sometimes a dome, in trees and shrubs. Eggs are brooded by the female.

CLASS	*Aves*
ORDER	*Passeriformes*
FAMILY	*Thraupidae*
GENERA	*62*
SPECIES	*271*

The superb tanager is confined to the forests of Brazil.

The female green honeycreeper is bright green with a paler breast. This fruit eater is larger than most other species.

The scarlet tanager breeds in North American woodlands and migrates to winter in South America. Breeding males are brilliantly scarlet and black.

The male pine grosbeak shows the bright plumage and thick bill typical of the group. It is primarily a seed eater and, like other species, is territorial.

CARDINALS AND GROSBEAKS

Cardinals and grosbeaks are mostly medium sized to small songbirds with stout, finchlike bills. Males are often brilliantly colored, but females are duller and brownish.

Cardinal bills are structured for crushing seeds, which are their staple diet in addition to some insects and fruit. Mostly tree-living, they forage in shrubbery and foliage.

Pairs bond strongly and may remain together year-round. Females are the nest builders, constructing a cup of plant fiber and tendrils in tussocks or low shrubberies on the ground; they incubate alone. Males help rear the young and may even continue feeding a first brood while their mates nest for a second time. Some North American species are migratory, but others are only locally nomadic.

These birds are found through North, Central and South America. Some from the north are migratory.

CLASS	Aves
ORDER	Passeriformes
FAMILY	Cardinalidae
GENERA	11
SPECIES	42

The male northern cardinal is distinctively red and crested; the female is olive brown with a reddish tinge.

313

GLOSSARY

adaptation A change in a bird's behavior or body that allows it to survive and breed in new conditions.

adaptive radiation A situation in which birds descended from a common ancestor evolve to exploit different ecological niches that are not being filled by other animals.

arboreal Living all or most of the time in trees.

bill The horny covering of the jaws of a bird, comprising two halves—the maxilla (upper) and the mandible (lower).

camouflage The colors and patterns of a bird that enable it to blend in with the background.

convergent evolution The situation in which unrelated birds develop similar traits to cope with similar evolutionary pressures.

courtship The behavior patterns that male and female birds display when they are trying to attract a mate.

crest A line of emergent feathers on the top of the head.

display Behavior used by a bird to communicate with its own species, or with other animals.

diurnal Active during daytime.

divergent evolution The situation in which two or more similar species become more and more dissimilar due to environmental adaptations.

egg tooth A sharp, tooth-shaped calcium deposit that grows on the tip of the bill of an embryonic bird.

embryo An unborn animal in the earliest stages of development.

exotic A foreign or non-native species of animal or plant, often introduced into a habitat by humans.

fledgling A young bird that has grown its first true feathers and has just left its nest.

fossil A remnant, impression, or trace of a plant or animal from a past geological age, usually found in rock.

Gondwana Ancient southern supercontinent, comprising the present-day continents of Australia, India, Africa, South America, and Antarctica.

habitat The area in which an animal naturally lives. Many different kinds of animals live in the same environment but each kind lives in a different habitat within that environment.

hatchling A bird that has recently hatched from its egg.

incubate To keep eggs in an environment, outside the female's body, in which they can develop and hatch.

insectivore An animal that eats insects or invertebrates.

introduced An animal or plant species imported from another place.

iridescent Showing different colors as light strikes from different angles.

juvenile A young bird that has grown its first set of fully functional feathers.

lek An arena or place where male birds of certain species congregate to compete in display to attract females for mating.

migration A usually seasonal journey from one habitat to another.

monogamous Describes male and female which pair to form a single couple.

niche The ecological position occupied by a species within an animal community.

nocturnal Active at night.

nomad A bird which lacks fixed territory, and wanders instead from place to place in search of food and water.

order A major group used in taxonomic classification. An order forms part of a class, and comprises one or more families.

pair bond A partnership maintained between a male and a female bird through one or several breeding attempts.

passerine Any species of bird belonging to the order Passeriformes. A passerine is often described as a songbird or a perching bird.

plumage The sum total of feathers on a bird's body.

polygamous Describes which males mate, usually temporarily, with more than one female at breeding time and vice versa.

predator A bird that lives mainly by killing and eating other animals.

regurgitate To bring food back up from the stomach to the mouth.

roost A place or site used by birds for sleeping. Also, the act of settling at such a place.

scavenger A bird that eats carrion—often the remains of animals killed by predators.

species A population of birds with very similar features that can breed together.

territory An area defended by a bird for its own exclusive use.

thermal A column of rising air, used by birds to gain height and on which some soar to save energy before gliding down.

transient A migrant bird in transit between its normal breeding and wintering distributions.

INDEX

ACKNOWLEDGMENTS

All maps and illustrations © Weldon Owen Pty Ltd. All photographs © istockphoto.com, except 22 tr Corbis;
228 Getty; 76 - 77 cb, 156 l, 206 cb, 206 bl, 230, 246, 249 Shutterstock; 258 bl, 259 bl Photolibrary.com;
169, 219 br, 224 t, 228 br, 231 bl, 232 bl, 234, 235 br, 237, 238, 239 br, 240 b, 241, 242, 243 br, 245, 254,
255 br, 264, 265 br, 280 Wikipedia.